. . . Papa's face tightened into a steel mask. He stepped into the cabin and returned with the old T-Barker shotgun. He broke open the breech and thumbed a green shell into each barrel. He strode down the ridge towards Boggy Creek.

Mama ran after him, her face lined with fear. "Henry!"

HILLBACK TO BOGGY

HILLBACK TO BOGGY

told by

JESS WILLARD SPEER

written by

BONNIE SPEER

RELIANCE PRESS

Also by Bonnie Speer
Errat's Garden
Benjamin Stanley Revett: Father of Gold Dredging
Heck Thomas, My Papa, with Beth Thomas Meeks
Moments In Oklahoma History, A Book of Trivia
Cleveland County (OK), Pride of the Promised Land
The Great Abraham Lincoln Hijack
The Killing of Ned Christie

Library of Congress CIP Data

Speer, Jess W. and Bonnie Speer

HILLBACK TO BOGGY

Includes Illustrations
1. Oklahoma--Memoir
2. Great Depression

LC 89-064193
ISBN 0-9619639-5-6 paper trade

Published by Reliance Press
1400 Melrose Drive
Norman, Ok 73069

Printed in the United States of America

Dedicated to all of my family and friends who lived it.

ACKNOWLEDGEMENTS

The writing of this book has taken at least ten years. Not the actual birth itself, but the gestation period. Throughout the book the sequence of the unfolding drama is pretty much as it happened, or as I remember.

This book is not written to embarrass anyone still living, who is portrayed in it; but instead to glorify those characters of my childhood, so that people far away from *Hillback To Boggy* geographically may see and extol their many virtues.

I am indebted to various siblings who remember this or that, or how an incident really happened. However, the real labor pains and physical drudgery of the birth (as usual) goes to the woman: Bonnie, my wife, who gathered together all the raw data and through a woman's magic made them into this book. She, more than anyone, has made these memories come alive again, thus preventing them being swept away and lost forever by the sands of time.

Jess "Tag" Speer
Norman, Ok
May 1991

TABLE OF CONTENTS

Twelve-year-old "Tag" Speer recalled in later years that those two years he spent on the Hillback to Boggy with his family, was the greatest adventure of his life.

Photo courtesy of Jess Speer.

Chapter 1

FORCED TO MOVE

I remember that time we lived in the tent. There were ten of us. It was during the heart of the Great Depression. In the fall of 1932, we lived in the tent pitched at the edge of a cotton patch in Western Oklahoma.

The wind blew and popped the sides of the tent, and made it creak until it seemed a thing alive. Dust motes built around the scraggly cotton stalks. Tumbleweeds and ticklegrass played leap frog across the barren fields and piled up under the barbed wire fence. Red flour dust swirled high into the sky, turned the sun bloody, and seeped into every corner of the tent. You could smell, feel, and taste the dust. Times were hard and jobs scarce.

By the first of December, we had the cotton picked. Papa let Opal, fourteen, Betty, ten, Hazel, eight, and me, twelve, ride the bus to school at Amber. The students made fun of us because we were poor and lived in a tent.

I had holes in my shoes and tripped over my socks, which kept creeping out of the holes. Opal, Betty, and Hazel shivered in their thin jackets. I wore an old sweater, which one of my older brothers had given me.

We didn't have anything for lunch except cornbread. I

let the girls have that and went out to play on the swings as if I didn't care.

Even so, I liked school, especially science and geography. I wanted to learn. I read all I could about building radios and idealized Robinson Crusoe.

One day, the teacher in my sixth grade class asked if anyone needed welfare clothes. If so, he could go to the principal's office and pick out some. No one raised his hand though some looked as if they could use the clothes. I did not want to admit being poor either. I sat hunched behind my history book, torn between the embarrassment of having to do so and knowing how much all our family needed clothing. Finally, gritting my teeth, I lifted my hand.

Some in the class snickered. I marched from the room feeling the heat coloring my cheeks and resenting the teacher for telling us the way she did.

In the principal's office, I dug through the welfare clothes. I found a pair of striped coveralls for four-year-old Pete, some nice dresses for Opal, Betty, and Hazel, and a shirt for me and one for Joe, who was fifteen. I stuffed the clothing into a paper sack.

The final bell sounded. I was glad. I didn't have to go back to the classroom and face everyone. I got on the school bus with my sack. One of the bigger boys grabbed it from me and held up a dress.

"Anyone for welfare clothes?" he taunted.

I lunged for the dress. "Give me that!"

The paper sack ripped. Feeling humiliated, I wadded up the garments and stuck them under my arm. The bus stopped to let us off at the edge of the cotton patch. I marched away, my throat aching with emotion, but determined no one was going to see me cry.

Hazel, a skinny little kid with short, black hair and black eyes, ran ahead, bursting to tell Mama and Papa I had been in a fight on the school bus. I wondered what they would say. Usually if I got in a fight at school, Papa would give me another licking, when I got home.

This time, when I gave the clothes to Mama and explained what happened, Papa, a tall, gaunt man, for once didn't say anything. That puzzled me. He just looked at me with a strange expression.

Mama, her brown hair drawn back in a bun from her thin, delicate face, patted my hand in reassurance. "Son, you did right."

Opal, Betty, and Hazel were tickled about getting the new dresses. Pete gazed at me in disappointment, his cast left eye squinting against the light, his thin face framed by his butcher-boy haircut. Then he spied the striped coveralls. He clutched them to his chest with a broad grin.

"T-Tag," he stuttered, "you my b-buddy some more."

That made everything worthwhile. I would have done it again, I thought.

After our supper of cornbread and milk, Papa sat with his cane-bottomed chair tipped back, staring at the tent wall for a long time. The pale light from the coal-oil lamp glistened in his black, bristly beard. He ran his large hands, with their stubby fingers, through his thin black hair. He held his corncob pipe between toothless gums. (He had false teeth but seldom wore them.) He pulled off his shoes, which he did whenever he could, for his feet ached a lot. Life had always been hard for him. He had raised twenty-five children, nine brothers and sisters after his father died, leaving Papa at the age of twelve as head of the family, and later, fourteen children of his own.

I hovered by the oil-drum stove, listening to the cold wind moaning about the tent. Mama sat at the table, mending a pair of Papa's threadbare overalls. Betty read her favorite book, *Bob and Betty White*. Opal sketched a portrait of Ginger Rogers on her Big Chief tablet. Hazel played doctor with Pete, while Joe strummed his guitar, and Frank, nineteen, played checkers with Perry, seventeen.

Abruptly, Papa slammed his big fist down upon the table, jiggling the lamp. "Confound it! I ain't goin' to gist sit around wearin' welfare clothes and starvin' to death. I'm movin' to Arkansas."

For a moment, no one said anything. In the silence, the wind snapped the sides of the tent, and everyone stared at Papa in surprise. Perry recovered first.

"Arkansas? Why go there?" he demanded.

Of a rebellious nature, Perry was always arguing with Papa to go someplace where Papa could make some money. Or else Perry teased Pete, or tried to correct the rest of us kids. In the flickering light, Perry looked a lot like Papa with his brown hair, high cheekbones, and dominate bulge at the back of his head, which all us Speer boys had. Perry had a sailor girl tattooed on his left arm. He wore dimestore glasses, behind which his eyes danced a lot. He was subject to ear infections. Papa had always felt sorry for Perry because of his eyes and ears, and guilty, as if somehow he were to blame. Now, Perry wore a cast on his left foot, following an accident, when he was out hoboing.

"How you goin' to make a livin'?" Perry went on. "Papa, if you're goin' to work your guts out, why don't you go to California, where there's some good land?"

"Be quiet, Perry," Frank interrupted, trying to keep the peace as usual. Quiet like Mama, Frank often helped her around the tent, washing dishes, carrying fuel, and getting water. He always acted considerate around womenfolk, and I thought he looked handsome, with his wavy, black hair. "Let Papa talk," Frank said. "Why not California, Papa?"

"Humph!" Papa squinched his eyes and snorted through his nose like a mule, as he often did, when annoyed. "Ever'body and his dog is goin' to California. Your mama's already wrote to your Uncle Alex and

Aunt Willie out there. They say, 'No, I'd think a long time before I come out here. You can't git work but gist a day-two at a time, and they's fifty people for ever' peach to pick out here. If you can make it somewhere else, you'd best go there.' I know where I can make it. Down in Arkansas, where I grew up as a kid."

"How're you goin' to eat?" Perry persisted.

"They's tall trees and streams," Papa answered. "Game in the woods, rabbits, squirrels and wild turkey. In the winter, they's furs, and fish in the creek. They's bee trees."

Perry shook his head. "Papa, it ain't goin' to be like when you was a boy. There's not goin' to be any game like there once was. The fish have all been caught and the game killed."

"Maybe the wild turkeys are gone," Papa conceded, "but I can live in the woods. A man would have wood and water. That's all we need. We can have a little garden along the creek bottom and maybe raise some cotton for cash."

"How are you goin' to git any land?" Perry argued. "How are you goin' to git any tools to work with? You can't just go up there and farm. You got to have a team; some mules to work with. You got to have a house. How you goin' to do it?"

"I don't know." Papa's face stiffened with a resolute look. "I'll cross that bridge when I come to it. I got faith in the Lord. I'll work."

Frank looked doubtful. "Papa, maybe we could go back to Tulsa and try to git on – "

"No," Papa interrupted, "they was nothin' there before. A hundred men for ever' job. I ain't goin' to take no handouts. It stands to reason, we'll be better off headin' the other direction."

Silence fell again. The cow chips crackled in the heating stove. A cricket crawled across the floor.

Opal flung down her pencil. "I don't want to go to the

woods! I want to go to school, have my friends, nice clothes, and learn to draw!" Her huge, dark eyes mirrored hurt beneath her curly, black hair. An attractive girl with a splash of freckles across her nose, Opal always differed with Papa about her clothes and art stuff.

Papa had never been too concerned about what we kids wanted, not that he was so hard-hearted, but because life itself was hard. "Opal," he said, "we can't stay here and starve to death."

Opal opened her mouth to retort, but Mama hushed her. Perry's hands balled in frustration, knowing it was useless to argue with Papa, when he made up his mind.

Mama's gray eyes filled with worry. "Henry, how're you goin' to get to Arkansas? There's no money, no way."

"I don't know," Papa repeated. "But I'll think of somethin'." With that, he tapped out his pipe and went to bed.

The rest of us soon followed suit. Frank and I slept in a pile of cottonseed in the old barn beyond the tent because there was not enough room in the tent. As I burrowed into the cottonseed and raked the warm kernels over me, my mind burned with visions of Arkansas.

Often, I had listened to Papa's stories about when he lived as a boy in the woods. This type of life sounded fine to me, like Robinson Crusoe. I could see myself shooting a squirrel and proudly toting it home for Mama to cook.

"Frank," I asked anxiously, "do you think Papa can find a way to move to Arkansas?"

For a moment, he gazed up at the rafters, casting shadows in the pale light of the smoky lantern. "I don't know." He sounded worried.

I knew what he was thinking. Frank was old enough to get married and be on his own. Perry had been out in the world and seen things, been chased off the freight trains by every railroad bull from "Denver Bobcat" to "Texas Slim," to hear Perry tell it.

Except for one short hobo trip to California, Frank had not been anywhere. He felt a responsibility to stay, and help the family make a living. Deep down though he considered himself trapped. He would rather go back to Tulsa, where there were picture shows, pretty girls, Post Toasties, and "store-bought" bread. Where Papa proposed going, we would be living like hermits in the woods. I sensed Frank wasn't so sure we wouldn't starve anyway.

"Well, we got to do somethin'," I said, echoing Papa.

Frank sighed. "Yeah, I know."

We talked for awhile about Papa. His father had been a circuit riding Baptist preacher. When Grandpa died of typhoid fever, Papa nearly died too. The family, hoping the fever would burn itself out, starved him for water. Ever since then, Papa had an obsession about water. His abiding dream was to earn an honest living, raise his "young uns" in the way of the Lord, and to someday own a place that had well water so cold it "hurt a-body's teeth."

Papa was never one to work much for the other fellow. Once, he owned a meat market in Fort Smith, Arkansas, but lost the store after allowing too much credit. For a time, he sharecropped in southeastern Oklahoma, where I was born.

When I was five, we moved near Tulsa. Papa farmed the old Penn Phillips place and raised a bumper cotton crop. Before he could get the cotton picked, the bottom fell out of the market.

Then the older kids, Houston, Bud, Avis, Vesta, Albert, and Herman began to marry and leave home. Papa bought some cows and hauled milk to Tulsa. He sold milk until the county health authorities told him he couldn't do that any more unless he put in a Grade A dairy. Papa didn't like people telling him how to run his business, so he sold his cows.

During the summer of 1929, Papa sold candy, floor sweep, and anything else he could. Frank and Perry delivered groceries on their bicycles. Opal won first prize at the county fair for one of her drawings. I roamed the streets, living an idealistic boyhood. Papa and Herman each bought a new Whippet automobile. Two months later, the stock market crashed.

Papa could hardly find a way to make a living after that. He bought roasting ears for ten cents a dozen; Joe and I peddled them for fifteen cents a dozen. I hated the peddling. I felt degraded by it.

Things got worse during the next two years. Papa would walk all the way across Tulsa looking for a job. By then, the whole country had grown desperate. Many headed for California, where they had heard there were good jobs picking oranges.

Perry hopped a freight train and went to California. After working on a dairy farm for awhile, he started home. One night, as he sat between two boxcars, he fell asleep. His foot slipped and got crushed between the couplings. Bud telegraphed him twenty dollars so he could come home on the bus.

Each day, Papa tramped the streets looking for work. Deeply religious he kept telling us to put our trust in the Lord, and we could make it. It seemed to me that the Lord wasn't helping anybody those days, least of all us.

Papa got tired of sitting around. He offered to work in a grocery store for nothing. Soon, the owner was paying him a dollar a day.

Then, the owner had to close his store. Papa lost his job. There weren't any more. Papa could not pay the four dollars a month rent the landlord asked, and winter was coming on.

One day, Papa, Frank, and a neighbor, Mr. Bush,

drove to Western Oklahoma to see if they could find some cotton to pick. A short time later, Papa sold off as much of our belongings as he could, and we moved to Amber. We left that new Whippet car sitting up on blocks.

We had a big tabernacle tent, about twenty by forty feet, which Bud and Charlie McClure, Avis' husband, had bought for ten dollars. We pitched the tent at the edge of the cotton patch.

We picked cotton for fifty cents a hundred pounds. By the first of December, the crop was picked. We had earned fifty dollars between us. Papa spent twenty-five dollars of this for a cow. By February, little of the rest of the money remained. Papa, Joe, and Frank walked everywhere trying to find a day's work. None could be found. Now, the cotton patch owner wanted us off the place. Papa was sure to fume at least once a day, "Ain't this a purty come-off?"

As Frank and I talked that night, I grew anxious again. "How is Papa goin' to do it? How're we goin' to git to Arkansas? How we goin' to keep from starvin'?"

Frank spoke quietly. "I don't know. Papa was never one to stay down long. It seems like he can always come up with somethin'."

"I hope so." I burrowed deeper into the warm cotton-seeds, and closed my eyes to dream about Arkansas, the land of plenty.

Chapter 2

THE TRIP

I didn't want to go to school next morning because of the welfare clothes. I was afraid the kids would laugh again.

Mama said, "You go to school all you can and learn something. Maybe someday you can make something out of yourself."

She had taught one year in a one-room country school. She was always telling us kids that and saving paper sacks for us to write on. Papa was the opposite. He didn't see much sense in our going to school. As long as "a-body" knew how to figure his paycheck and read the Bible, he thought that was enough.

I decided to take Mama's advice and got ready for school. There wasn't much to do around the tent anyway except worry about how hungry I was all the time and how we were going to get to Arkansas.

Papa and Frank had got up early and gone off. Mama didn't know where. Papa wasn't one to tell her his business. Perry was packing his clothes.

"I ain't goin' to Arkansas and starve," he said, stumping around on his cast. "I'm goin' up to Tulsa and hunt a job. At least there you can get a box of Post Toasties and a can of Pork and Beans once in awhile. That's better'n starvin' in the woods."

"Oh, Perry, how do you know?" I defended. "Papa knows how to live in the woods. Why don't you stay and help the family once in awhile, instead of runnin' off all the time?"

Perry turned on me. "Look, who's skinnin' this cat, you or me?"

He snapped the lid shut on his cardboard suitcase, kissed Mama, and headed for the door. Mama didn't say much as Perry came and went a lot, and it was one less mouth to feed. Still, I knew she worried about him.

When Opal, Betty, Hazel, and I went out to catch the bus, Perry was already a black speck down the road. The girls wore their new dresses and were proud of them, until we got on the bus.

"Got your new welfare dresses on?" some smart aleck popped off.

Opal's cheeks reddened. She didn't say anything, but I could see she was trying to hold back the tears. Opal had always taken a lot of pride in her appearance. It was hard for her to accept the destitute position our family found itself in now. For me, I could never understand why some kids had to be so cruel to others.

I patted Opal's hand. "That's all right, 'Tubby.' Someday you'll be a famous artist. Then you'll show 'em."

She was tall and thin, but we called her 'Tubby' sometimes, because once she had put a kitten under a tub and let the kitten smother.

At school, the day dragged. I kept worrying about how we were going to get to Arkansas. There, we would not have to worry about welfare clothes. I sure hoped Papa and Frank came up with something.

The next few days passed and nothing happened. I began to think Mama was right. There wasn't any way we could get to Arkansas.

On the third evening, when we got off the school bus, Hazel ran on ahead. A feisty little thing, she could be a good buddy and wouldn't tell on me unless she got mad. Tiny and cute, she looked a lot like Mama with dark eyes beneath her short, dark bangs.

Betty would tell on me sometimes. She had brown eyes and short brown hair. She did not like wearing overalls to the cotton patch. Soon as she got to the tent, she changed into a dress. She was good in her school work, and like Opal, worried about nice clothes and a pretty home.

Me, I had dark brown hair, which never looked combed, and I was a little on the chubby side. I got my nickname "Tag," from hanging after Mama all the time, when I was little. I looked like Papa with a pointed face, large head, and squinty brown eyes. I wore patched blue overalls with the legs rolled up, a blue denim shirt, and whatever kind of shoes the kids in Tulsa gave me. I had a checkered cap with a broken bill that I wore cocked on the side of my head. That was the way James Cagney and the other movie stars in the gangster pictures wore their caps. However, movie stars were far from my mind at the moment as I worried about going to Arkansas.

Ahead of the rest of us as usual, Hazel came to a sudden halt. "Looky there!"

Startled, I glanced up. Beside the tent stood an old 1927 Model-T truck with wooden sideboards and a visor on the square cab. The black paint looked worn and the tires thin, but I thought it the most beautiful truck I had ever seen. Papa and Frank had the hood up, checking the motor.

I ran towards them hollering, "Where did you git her? How much did she cost? We goin' to Arkansas?"

Papa reared up under the hood, smashing his uncreased, black, felt hat, which was discolored with sweat and dust. He snorted. "Arkansas, your hindleg! You John Brown young uns do beat all I ever saw. Git back and stay outa the way!"

I shied around to the side of the truck. We kids were all over it, trying to see. Frank opened the door and adjusted a lever.

I whispered, "'Rusty,' we goin' to Arkansas?" We called him 'Rusty Guts' sometimes, because once when he was young and had an upset stomach, he told Mama his guts were rusty.

"Looks like it," Frank replied.

I could see right off he was not nearly as excited about the prospect as I. "How did Papa git the truck?"

"Traded the cow for it and got five dollars to boot."

I glanced around to where our blue jersey cow usually grazed, and she was gone. For a moment, I wondered what we were going to eat. That cow gave four gallons of milk a day. Sometimes, that was all we had to go with our cornbread. I decided Papa could worry about that.

"When are we leavin'?"

Papa overheard me and lifted his head. "Tomorrow. Ain't no use hangin' around here. You John Brown young uns git inside and help your Mama pack."

Inside the tent, we found Joe and Mama trying to work with little Pete underfoot. Joe was turned a little different from the rest of us. Quiet, he always did what Papa told him. He helped Mama and was good in his school work, though he didn't get to go to school, when we lived in the tent. He had black hair and brown eyes and was very self-conscious of his crooked teeth. He tried to hide them with his tongue when he smiled. Joe and I were good buddies.

Pete, he was just a silly little kid who didn't know anything, but to goose somebody with something then giggle. Right now he was poking Mama with a long-handled spoon while she was trying to wrap some old clothes around the dishes and pack them in a tub.

Mama took a swat at him. "You little scamp. Betty,

Hazel -- somebody take care of this young un awhile. The rest of you help Joe and me pack."

That I was more than willing to do.

The next morning, we all helped load the truck. How we got everything on it amazed me. We had the Victrola, our prized possession, which Papa had bought new a few years ago, and a collection of country-western and religious records. Then there were the table and chairs, a bench, Mama's sewing machine, our beds, a small iron cookstove, and a vertical wardrobe.

Up behind the cab, Papa made a little den, where Mama and we kids could ride on a mattress. We took down the tent, folded it, and loaded it on the truck. Nothing remained but a hard-packed square on the ground, where the tent had stood. We shivered in the cold.

Papa motioned with his big hand. "Load up. We'll head toward Chickasha and stay all night with the Beards, then head out for Scott County first thing in the mornin'."

We kids and Mama climbed into our little den. Frank took the steering wheel with Papa beside him. Arkansas, here we come, I thought.

It was late afternoon before we reached Chickasha. That night Papa and Mr. Beard gassed about Arkansas and what a good thing Papa was doing.

"I'd go to Arkansas myself," Mr. Beard said, "but I don't know how to live off the land like you do."

"Well, ever'thing'll be a'right," Papa said, "soon as the Democrats get back in office next month."

Mr. Beard nodded. "Seems like the only way this country is ever gonna get headed around is to get them blue-bellied Republicans out and the Democrats back in."

Neither of them knew anything about the incoming president, Franklin D. Roosevelt, except he had been governor of New York State. Both believed anybody would be better than Mr. Hoover, whose prosperity was always "just around the corner."

"Why," Papa said, "in a big city like Tulsa, a-body could get twenty cents an hour, when they wasn't no Depression. Right after the war, it wasn't uncommon for a guy to make five dollars a day gist cutting bo-darc posts. If the country can gist git Hoover out of the White House and git a Democrat in there, it gist stands to reason things'll pick up."

We slept on the floor that night. When Papa woke us at four a.m., Mama and Mrs. Beard were making breakfast.

It was still dark when we piled back into the truck. Mama pulled the quilts up around us kids to ward off the cold. We headed north towards Oklahoma City.

The old truck creaked and groaned under its burden, and blue smoke trailed from the exhaust pipe. The sun came up. The engine clattered, and the radiator got hot. We hadn't gone twenty miles when a tire blew out. Frank eased the truck over to the side of the road, the flat tire thumping and washtubs rattling.

Papa and Frank walked a half-mile to a filling station. Papa bought some Camel tire patching and a boot for the tire. Joe helped Papa and Frank fix the tire.

We went on. At noon, Papa bought some crackers and bologna, and we ate under a tree. An hour later, we crawled through Oklahoma City on Route 66. Occasionally, I saw an old jalopy or truck, loaded down like ours, heading west in the other lane. The men and women wore the same worried expressions I'd seen on Mama's and Papa's faces lately.

"Where you reckon they's goin'?" I asked nobody in particular.

"California, I 'magine," Joe answered.

I didn't think they looked as if they had much chance of making it.

East of Oklahoma City, the flat prairie land gave way

to the tree-covered hills of Eastern Oklahoma. Things were looking better already, I thought.

About two o'clock, we had another flat. Everyone piled out, and Frank and Papa fixed it. We went on. Frank had to stop often to let the radiator cool. Joe and I took turns riding in the cab with Papa and Frank.

Late in the afternoon, the motor began hammering. Frank pulled over to the side of the road once more. It seemed to me as if we had spent more time pulling over all day than driving.

Frank checked the oil. "She's low."

Papa sighed. "Well, we got to have some."

They set off down the road again. In an hour, they returned with two quarts of cheap oil. Frank poured the oil into the engine. The sun stood near the western horizon.

Mama looked anxious. "Henry, what're we goin' to do about supper?"

Papa glanced at the sky. "Well, I reckon we're goin' to have to have somethin'. We'll stop at the next store."

At the store, he bought some more bologna, light bread, a lantern globe, and gas. His money was going fast. We parked beside the road again. Over a small campfire, Mama made coffee in a gray enameled pot and fried some potatoes.

After we ate, Papa rose and glanced around. Dark had come; no light gleamed in the distance. "We might as well keep driving all night," he spoke wearily. "We've got to git there. Got nowhere else to sleep anyways."

Frank nodded. "Might as well be drivin', as sittin' 'side the road a freezin'."

Mama cleaned up the dishes and put out the fire. We got back into the truck.

My teeth chattered as I crawled under the quilt. "How far do you think we come, Mama?"

She drew her coat closely around her to ward off the cold. "I don't know. Maybe fifty or sixty miles."

"Are we nearly to Arkansas?"

She drew a deep breath. "I don't know that either, son. We'll be there when we get there."

Frank drove back onto the highway, turning left on Oklahoma 270. The feeble headlights picked up the blacktop. Long-eared jackrabbits zig-zagged in front of us, and darted into the brush. The old truck rattled, creaked, groaned, and hammered. The cold wind blew against my face. I huddled up beside the other kids, hoping it was warmer in Scott County, Arkansas, where we were headed.

Sometime in the night, I awoke. Mama sat up. The motor was banging and clanging like an elephant with horseshoes dancing on a brick street. I peered into the cab. In the reflected light, I could see Frank gripping the wooden steering wheel, listening. Papa motioned to Frank. Frank turned off the ignition switch. The truck bounced off the blacktop and rattled to a halt on the shoulder of the road. The old truck creaked wearily, and settled into its track, steam hissing from the radiator.

"What's wrong, Mama?" I asked.

"I don't know."

The other kids stirred. Papa untangled his long legs and crawled out of the cab. The torn sleeve of his old suit coat fluttered in the cold night air.

Papa snorted. "Ain't this a purty come off. Larie, you might as well pile out, and we'll build a fire. Sounds like this old truck's blowed-up-Doogan."

Mama raised her small frame from the quilts. "Is it bad, Henry?"

"Sounds like she's throwed a rod. If it ain't one John Brown thing, it's another. I know that in my time, I do git aggravated."

Having patience was not one of Papa's better virtues.

We climbed out of the truck. After we relieved ourselves in the woods, the girls on one side of the road and the boys on the other, we all helped drag up deadwood and brush. Soon, Papa had a fire roaring.

"Larie, might as well put on the coffee pot," he said.

The perking coffee along with the hickory and cedar smoke smelled good. The fire chased back the night and cold. Mama poured each of us some coffee. We huddled around the fire, Papa and Frank watching the old truck. I couldn't imagine why. The truck wasn't going anywhere, and goodness knows, we didn't have anything anybody would want to steal.

Papa's fifty-nine years sat heavily upon his bent shoulders. "Sometimes it does seem like the good Lord gives me more than my share of burdens," he said.

"Do you think you can fix the truck?" Mama asked.

"I don't know. We'll see 'bout it come daylight. Meanwhile, we might as well try to git some rest."

Mama and Joe got the quilts from the truck. Papa threw another big chunk of wood on the fire. We all settled down as comfortably as we could.

The wind died down a little. Stars twinkled in the clear, cold night, and off in the woods an owl hooted. Pete whimpered. Mama pulled him into her lap.

She rocked back and forth, singing softly, "*Rock of ages, cleft for me . . .*"

I didn't know if she was singing more to quiet her own fears or those of little Pete.

Chapter 3

DOWN AND OUT

Thin light filtered through the barren post oaks, when I awoke next morning. The truck sat near the crest of a hill. Mama busied herself about the campfire making breakfast. Papa and Frank squatted nearby, drinking coffee and discussing what they were going to do.

"Near as I can figger," Papa said, "we must be 'bout two mile from Calvin. The stores'll open soon. We'll walk in and see if we can git a wrench or two to fix the truck."

"You got the money, Papa?" Frank asked.

"Do or don't, we got to have 'em. We got to do somethin'."

Mama handed them each a plate. They fell to eating. When through, Papa wiped the back of his hand across his mouth and black, stubbly beard and rose.

"Larie, we'll git back soon as we can."

He and Frank took off up the road, Papa slinging his long arms the way he always did when walking fast.

Mama poured herself a cup of coffee. I knew she wouldn't eat until she was sure there was enough to feed everyone. She noticed I was awake.

"You sleep all right?"

"A cottonseed pile is warmer and softer," I said.

Her gray eyes shadowed. "'Spect so. Maybe someday we can all have a decent bed again."

She glanced at the truck. I read her thoughts.

"You think Papa and Frank can fix it?" I asked.

She shook her head, and a loose hairpin fell out of her uncombed hair. "I don't know. I just don't know what we'll do if they can't."

At her dismal tone, I envisioned a dark, hopeless future for us. I wondered if we might not starve to death right here beside the road. I hated President Hoover; I hated this mean old Depression. It didn't seem right that a man like Papa, who was willing to work, couldn't find a job to feed his family. I felt trapped, not being able to help, though I was only twelve. Maybe Perry had the right idea. Maybe we should have all gone back to Tulsa. I wondered if Perry was up there right now, eating Post Toasties and Pork and Beans.

My stomach growled at the thought. 'Tag,' I scolded myself, 'ain't no use wanting something you ain't got. Like Mama says, spit in one hand and wish in the other, see which one gits full first. Be glad for what you got. Papa will figure out somethin'.'

I crawled out of my quilt and stood shivering in the cold. "Can I have a pancake?"

The other kids awoke. Mama fed us dry pancakes made from flour mixed with a little water. We gulped them down with hot coffee.

After breakfast, Joe and I helped Mama carry water from a nearby stream so we could clean up a bit.

"We may be poor but we ain't going dirty," she said.

Joe and I dragged up some more wood. Opal helped Mama wash the dishes, then went off and sat on a rock. She was sure getting moody, didn't want to talk to anybody. She dipped snuff, a habit she'd picked up from Mama. Because of this, sometimes we kids called Opal "Snuffy" instead of Tubby, teasing her.

Betty and Hazel found some hickory nuts. Pete whined around and hung onto Mama's dresstail. Mama felt his forehead. "This baby's running a fever. That's all we need, everybody come down sick, getting out like this."

The morning warmed a little. We all cleaned up. Then, Joe and I talked about things we were going to order someday from the catalog, when we got rich. I thought Papa and Frank were never going to get back. Finally, Hazel saw them.

"Yonder they come!"

Papa and Frank carried a couple of wrenches and a new gasket for the truck. Papa's face looked drawn.

"Took 'bout the last penny I had. I got a whole nickel left."

Mama didn't say anything, but I could sense what she was thinking, how were we going to get to Arkansas?

Papa and Frank each gulped down a cup of coffee then went to the truck. Joe and I tagged along.

Frank slid under the truck and felt the greasy pan.

Papa handed him a crescent wrench. "Tag, git me a bucket. We got to save the oil. We can't buy no more."

I jumped to get the bucket. Frank loosened the oil plug with the wrench. The oil ran down his arm and into the bucket. He backed out the pan bolts evenly.

Papa squatted beside the truck. "Try to save that gasket if you can. We'll take this new un back."

"Can't, Papa," Frank said. "She's too brittle."

Papa grunted as if he half expected that. "When a man's down, he's down. Anything I can do?"

"Soon as the oil's all out, you can help me drop the pan."

Papa crawled under the truck. They let the pan down easy, and laid it on the ground. Neither Papa nor Frank knew much about working on an automobile. Papa rattled the connecting rod against the shaft. It was loose and the bearing about burned up.

"Looks like that might be the trouble," he said.

"What do you reckon caused it?" Frank asked.

"Don't know. She was using oil, when we got her. Maybe we let the oil get too low."

"Maybe we can tighten that rod a little and git her going," Frank suggested.

"Maybe," Papa spoke wearily. He handed Frank another wrench.

Frank tightened the rod.

"If you git it too tight, she'll burn out for shore," Papa warned.

"Yeah, and if I git it too loose, she'll hammer out," Frank returned.

"Well, either way, I guess we ain't got much to lose."

Frank did the best he could. He patted the new gasket in place. He lifted the pan and held it while Papa tightened the bolts with the crescent wrench.

They crawled from beneath the truck. Papa poured the oil back into the motor. Frank inspected the pan for leaks.

"Looks like she's holding."

"A'right, try the motor," Papa said.

The motor caught with a roar, and black smoke poured from the exhaust.

Papa waved his hand. "Idle it down!"

He and Frank listened to the motor.

"Still sounds loose as a goose to me." Frank glanced up the road. "If we got any long hills to climb – " He left his words hanging, his meaning clear.

Papa's eyes squinched. "Dog tick it!" he fussed. "If it ain't one John Brown thing after another. We can't hang around here. We got to try it. Larie, you got anything to eat? We got enough gas to git on down to your brother Bryan's at Ashland. He's done blacksmithing and knows some about cars. Maybe he can help us git this John Brown truck fixed so we can git on to Arkansas."

I wanted to believe him, but didn't see how without any money. Mama gave everybody a piece of cornbread and the last of the coffee. I choked the cold food down, wishing I had a piece of sidemeat to go with it.

We climbed back into the truck. Frank eased onto the highway. The engine hammered. The truck crept over the hill and coasted down the other side, trailing smoke.

We crossed the South Canadian River and went through Calvin. The truck got hot, and Frank had to stop several times to let it cool.

Pete fretted. Mama tried to soothe him.

When we got to Stuart, where I had been born, Papa motioned for Frank to stop. Papa went inside a grocery store and came back with a nickel's worth of graham crackers. He handed them to Mama.

"That baby's mostly hungry." He got back in the truck, his face angry and bewildered.

Mama gave Pete a cracker and one to Hazel and Betty. She offered me one. It tempted me, but I shook my head.

"Better save 'em for Pete." I knew we were broke and busted.

Uncle Bryan lived in the oak-covered hills about fifteen miles south of Stuart. It took us about three hours to get there. He, Aunt Eula, Hughie Avis, and Bernice lived in a two-room, unpainted, shanty with a sheet-iron roof.

Uncle Bryan and Aunt Eula were tickled to see us.

"Y'all git out and come on in!" Uncle Bryan called out in his slow, hill-country drawl.

We piled into the house with a lot of noise and confusion. Uncle Bryan was a tall, humped-back fellow. He wore overalls, blue denim shirt, billed cap, and smoked a pipe. Aunt Eula, short and stocky, had gray eyes. She wore her brown hair pulled back in a knot. Hughie Avis, a tow-headed kid of seven, whined, when he talked. Bernice was a chubby girl of five.

"Whar y'all headin', Hen-a-ree?" Uncle Bryan drawled.

"Arkansas," Papa said. He told him about the truck breaking down. "I was hopin' you might help us fix it."

"Wal, I been workin' here on dis place for Dick O'Daniels fer fifty cents a day. But I might take a look at hit tomorry, if'n we git through plowin' over yonder."

Papa nodded. "I'd be obliged. I hate puttin' you out this way, pilin' in on you – "

"Now don't you be a frettin' about it," Aunt Eula interrupted. "You uns gist make yourself at home. Yer welcome to stay as long as ye need to. We'll make out."

"Much obliged, Eular," Papa said.

Uncle Bryan suggested Papa better put the truck in the barn in case it rained. They could work on the truck there out of the cold.

Uncle Bryan had killed hogs. For supper, Aunt Eula made biscuits, light as store-bought bread, fried potatoes, and some sidemeat. All of us ate as if we were half-starved, which truth to tell, we were.

After supper, Papa took off his shoes and settled back to visit with a look of half-way contentment. There were two things which Papa greatly enjoyed: having plenty to eat and a chance to talk a lot.

That night, Aunt Eula made us all a pallet on the floor. Next morning, when we got up, a drizzly rain fell.

"Wal, Hen-a-ree," Uncle Bryan drawled, "looks like we might git to work on that truck of yourn today."

Papa grinned for the first time in days. "Sometimes, the Lord does furnish miracles."

Mama helped Aunt Eula fix breakfast, while Pete clung to her skirt. "I'm sure thankful they got the truck in out of the wet. Would've ruined what little we got, especially that Victrola."

Aunt Eula looked up quickly. "Y'all got a Victrola?"

Mama nodded with pride. "Nice collection of records, too."

Aunt Eula sighed. "I was a-tellin' my sister Arty, gist

the other day, 'Arty,' – said – 'I shore lak to hear gospel singin' on the Victrola,' – said."

"So does Henry," Mama said. "That Victrola's his pride and joy."

After we ate, Joe and I tagged the men out to the barn to see about the old truck. Uncle Bryan was a good mechanic. He and Frank crawled under the truck and dropped the pan. Uncle Bryan shook the connecting rod.

"Babbit's gone out of de berin's, Hen-a-ree."

Papa peered under the truck. "Think you can fix 'er?"

"Dis temporary. Tag, run to the house and tell your Aunt Eulie to send me a meat skin."

I couldn't imagine why he wanted that. When I got back with it, Uncle Bryan cut a thin strip from the bacon rind. He wrapped the strip around the connecting rod and tightened the rod. He and Frank put the pan back on and poured the oil back into the motor.

"Now, start her up, Frank," Uncle Bryan said.

The motor turned over a couple of times, roared, pinged a time or two, then settled down. Papa grinned.

Uncle Bryan shook his head, discouraging him. "No, Hen-a-ree, it won't hold long. Soon as 'at meat skin wears out, 'at rod'll go agin. I wouldn't start out in this truck if'n I was you. You git down in dem mountains by Wilburton, she's liable to fly apart. Better git shed of this thang fust chanct you git."

Papa's face clouded. I had a feeling we were never going to get to Arkansas.

During the next two weeks, we stayed with Uncle Bryan and Aunt Eula, fourteen of us crowded together in that little house. Papa didn't know which way to turn. He and Frank walked everywhere looking for work. Papa knew we couldn't keep on staying with Uncle Bryan and Aunt Eula. They were having hard enough time trying to live as it was.

One day, Papa and we boys borrowed Dick O'Daniel's

axe and saw. We went over in the woods on the county line and cut Uncle Bryan a couple of ricks of stove wood. That was the least we could do, Papa said. Next morning, when Mr. O'Daniels saw the wood, he told Papa he'd give him a dollar for two ricks. Then Virgil Gould, Uncle Bryan's brother-in-law, offered Papa a Rhode Island rooster for a rick of wood. All this pleased Papa. Still, it wasn't finding us a place to live.

One night, Papa said, "Bryan, I been thinkin'. If I can gist git into the woods and near water, I got that tent. That county line road's not open, and they's water. Why can't I set that tent over there in the woods? Ain't nobody goin' to tell me to take it off, 'cause it belongs to the county. We could clear up a little patch for a garden."

"Wal, Hen-a-ree, you kin shore give it a whirl. I don't think anybody'll bother ye over dere."

"Good, Frank and me'll walk over there first thing in the mornin' and have a look at her."

My heart jumped with joy. I had been disappointed that we couldn't go on to Arkansas, but living here in the Oklahoma woods would be just about as good, I reasoned.

The next morning, Papa and Frank walked over to the county line road. They were back by noon. Papa shook his head.

"It's too wet and swampy back in there. We'd all git the chills. 'Sides, the brush is too thick. We could never git it cleared in time to make a garden."

My heart sank. It seemed there was nothing we could do.

Uncle Bryan studied on the problem a bit. "Hen-a-ree, you been to see old man Reeder yet? You know, he's been all over this country with them gold huntin' notions of his'n. He gist might know of a place whar you could camp."

Mr. Reeder was step-father-in-law to my sister Vesta.

Papa knew Mr. Reeder from when he lived here before. The Reeders had been to our house in Tulsa. They had three boys about the same age as Joe, Frank, and me, and two girls.

"I hadn't thought 'bout Mr. Reeder," Papa said. "I'll go see him tomorrow. If anybody knows, he will."

Next morning, Papa considered taking the truck. Uncle Bryan advised against it.

"Ye git into 'at blue mud on Hickerson Hill and have a hard pull, ye might throw 'at rod."

So Papa and Frank took out on foot again. I wandered around the ponds behind Uncle Bryan's house all morning, waiting eagerly for them to get back. They arrived in the middle of the afternoon with Albert Reeder, in a green wagon drawn by a team of matched mules.

Albert was about Frank's age with near-sighted, brown eyes and dark brown hair combed back "pump style." He wore his cap set squarely on his head.

"Howdy, Albert," Joe greeted. "What'cha know?"

"Aw, nothin'" Albert drawled, "'cept what I know on myself and I ain't tellin' that."

We went into the house. Papa told us Albert Reeder had squatter's rights to a little clearing on a hill back to Boggy Creek. Papa was talking trade to him for the clearing.

Mama looked puzzled. "What have we got to trade, Henry?"

"The Victrola." His lips quivered a little. I knew he had mixed emotions about this. "Albert plays the gittar. When he heard we had that Victorla and all them records, he said he might be willin' to trade that clearin' for the Victrola and ten dollars."

"We haven't got ten dollars," Mama reminded.

"Oh, I told Mr. Speer y'all could work that out," Albert put in quickly. "I ain't pressin' for the money. Say, y'all got that record, *Wildwood Flower*?"

"I 'magine," Joe acknowledged with a grin.

"I shore do like that tune." Albert broke into song while playing an imaginary guitar: *"Oh, the roses so red, and the lilies so fair . . ."*

Papa cleared his throat. "I looked at the clearin', Larie. It's about a mile west of the main, sandy road. They's eight to ten acres cleared up in there with a brush fence around it. It has two log cribs. We might live in one of them. They's a family there now, but they's supposed to git off. That's who Albert got the clearin' from. West of the clearin', about two hundred yards back in the pines, they's a spring. I tasted the water. It's pure, cold, and sweet. Albert says the spring runs all year. I seen squirrels in the woods. We can set the tent down in the clearin' and start farmin' that land right off without havin' to clear it. We can plant a garden next month."

I hung on Papa's words. I could see he was all fired up about the clearing. It sounded good to me, too.

However, Mama looked doubtful. "Henry, whose land is it? You can't just move onto somebody's land."

"It's nobody's land," Papa argued. "It's gist sittin' there. Sam Pace, the man livin' there, cleared it. Albert traded him a sow and two pigs for his rights. Now, I'm tradin' Albert the Victrola and ten dollars for his rights."

"Henry," Mama insisted, "even if it is ten miles back in the bojacks and it is just sitting there, somebody must own it. Probably some oil company in Tulsa or Oklahoma City."

Papa squinched his eyes and snorted. "Larie," he said, the edge in his voice letting her know he didn't appreciate a woman trying to run his business. "You and me and these young uns have got to have somewhere to squat. I reckon that place is gist as good as any."

With that, as far as Papa was concerned, the case was closed. I knew Papa didn't mean to be dishonest, moving in on somebody's property that way, but like a lot of other people he was caught in a bind.

We had brought the Victrola into the house so Aunt Eula and the others could enjoy the music a bit. Now I stood by Mama as Papa and Frank helped Albert carry the Victrola and records out to the wagon.

Tears glistened in Opal's eyes as she watched. "There goes the last decent thing we had."

Mama squeezed her hand in understanding.

Chapter 4

THE REEDERS

Papa wanted to get an early start for the clearing next morning. However, Hazel got up sick. With her and Pete both whining around, by the time we got in the truck, the sun was up, thawing the frozen ground.

Uncle Bryan stood in the yard bidding us goodbye. "Hen-a-ree, wifey and me'll make it up dere in a few days to see how ye gittin' along."

Papa nodded, impatient to be off. "Much obliged for ever'thing."

Aunt Eula came running from the house with a middling of meat and a small sack of flour. "Here, you uns take this."

Papa's Adam's apple bobbed. "I hate to sponge off of you."

Uncle Bryan spit on the ground. "'At's all right, I got credit at Ashland."

At last we got going, the truck swaying and creaking.

"Ye might hev trouble gittin' up Hickerson Hill!" Uncle Bryan hollered after us.

The road from Uncle Bryan's led west across the brush choked Ranch Creek bottoms. The road was sandy and easy going until we reached Billy Hawkins' place. Billy Hawkins was a Choctaw Indian who lived in a small rundown house with a crooked stovepipe.

Billy Hawkins stood on the porch, and waved to us.

He had long braids, a dark leather cap, and a large mole on the side of his nose. Mrs. Hawkins chopped wood in the yard. She wore a denim jacket, a leather cap, and a pair of men's workshoes. A one-eyed dog crawled from under the porch and barked at us.

Papa motioned to Frank to stop the truck. "Howdy, Billy Hawkins," Papa called out. "You 'member me?"

"Yeah, me know. Henry Speer," he said in broken English. "Where you live now?"

"Fixing to set down on that clearing west of Mr. Reeder's."

Billy Hawkins nodded in approval. "Good squirrel huntin' in there."

"Think we can make it up Hickerson Hill?" Papa asked.

"Maybe yes, maybe no. Road slicker'n owl grease. You get stuck, my wife, he come with pony, yank you out."

"Thank ye, Billy,"

We went on, Joe and I snickering at the way Billy Hawkins talked.

A half-mile west of Billy Hawkins', we crossed a small branch that ran across the road. The truck bogged down in the mud.

Papa crawled out of the cab, fuming. "Dog tick it! Ever'body pile out and push 'cept Larie and them two sick uns."

Papa and Joe found a pole and pried under the axle. Everyone else pushed. The truck climbed out of the mud.

At the next corner, we turned north. Hickerson Hill lay before us, a long, steep slope of blue clay, deeply rutted. A ditch ran along each side of the hill. The truck skidded. Frank settled the wheels into the ruts. We inched up the hill, the blue clay clinging to the wheels. The truck bogged down. Frank rocked the truck back and forth, and we crept forward again. The backend slid sideways.

Papa jumped out of the truck. "You kids git out and push!"

The truck refused to budge. Frank put the gear into reverse to back down and to get another shot at the hill. The truck picked up speed and slid backwards out of control.

Papa ran after it. "Hold her, Newt! Hold her!"

"The brakes are gone!" Frank hollered in panic.

Mama raised to her knees, clutching Pete and Hazel to her. The truck careened, threatening to overturn. Frank tried to hold it in the ruts. The truck tipped. In desperation, Frank cramped the wheels. The rear end of the truck whipped about, went into the ditch, and came to a sudden stop at an angle. Mama climbed out of the truck, shaking.

"Now you played hob!" Papa shouted at Frank. "What'd you run in the ditch for?"

"To keep from killin' Mama!" Frank shouted back.

Papa blinked, absorbing this information. "Well, I guess that *was* quick thinkin'. But how're we going to git it outa there?"

"You want Tag and me to go after Billy Hawkins?" Joe offered.

Papa shook his head. "Naw, he couldn't do much with gist a pony. Better head on over to Reeders'. Git Albert to bring his mules."

Joe and I took off at once.

"It's two and a half miles. Don't fool around," Papa called after us.

We broke into a trot. We passed three houses and turned west. The road led past the Bohannon church and schoolhouse. Because it was Saturday, nobody played in the schoolyard. I worried that the Reeders might be gone when we got there. We left the road and cut across a cane field.

Finally, we reached the Reeder's. The house sat back from the road. To the west stood an old barn and two log cribs with sheet iron roofs. The mules stood in the horselot and Mr. Reeder's black buggy sat before the white house with its dog trot and long porch. I grinned in relief, knowing the Reeders were home.

A collie and a little crooked-tailed feist rose from the porch and barked.

"Hello!" Joe called out.

Albert Reeder stepped out of the house, followed by Loren Reeder. Loren was about Joe's age, husky and good looking. He wore striped overalls and parted his thick, brown hair on the side.

Albert squinted in his near-sightedness, then recognized us. "What're you boys up to? Come in! Come in!"

Joe opened the gate. The dogs sniffed at our heels. Joe explained about the truck getting stuck. "We come to see if we could borrow your mules to pull us out."

"Shore thing," Albert said without hesitation. "Loren and me'll take old Babe and Kate over there with a trace chain and have you out quicker than a squirrel can skin a hickory. You wanta come in and get warm first?"

"Naw," Joe said. "We better git right back. I'll help hitch the team. Tag can git warm if he wants to."

That suited me. I was eager to see the Reeders again, especially J.W.

The Reeder family sat around the fireplace. The living room was papered with gray building paper studded with metal discs and the pine floor had been scoured white.

Mrs. Reeder, a stoop-shouldered woman, with a knot of graying brown hair at the back of her neck and a ruddy complexion, rose in greeting. "Tag, how's your mama? Jay, Nora, you kids get Tag a chair.

J.W., twelve, a small, shy looking kid with shaggy, blond hair and green eyes, shoved a cane-bottomed chair toward me. He wore his overall legs rolled up and cowhide shoes with socks that didn't match.

Zenora, eleven, had brown hair and beady eyes like a mouse. Pansy, the oldest, wore thick glasses like Albert.

Mr. Reeder was a scrawny looking old man with a bald head and scraggly, yellow mustache. He wore a yellow vest and a watch fob with "K.K.K." on it. In his younger days, he had been a Texas Ranger, but now he was in poor health. His black eyes gleamed with interest. "You sorry-looking Petes, what devilment you boys up to?"

I twisted my cap in my hand. "Aw, Frank was drivin', and our truck slid off in a ditch."

"I don't doubt it, nary a bit." Mr. Reeder chuckled. "Boys don't know how to do anythang but gad around. Gittin' stuck, that's all them automobiles is good for. Hah! You ort to get a buggy like I got."

"'Spect so," I said.

"Don't let him kid you, Tag," Mrs. Reeder said.

I nodded. I had always liked Mr. and Mrs. Reeder. Each had been married before. Between them they had sixteen kids. Only five remained at home.

"How's Vestie and Virgil?" Mrs. Reeder asked.

"A'right, I reckon," I answered. "We ain't heard from them much since we left Tulsa. It costs three cents to mail a letter."

"I know. Ain't that a sight? This Depression's hurting ever'body."

"Depression?" Mr. Reeder said. "Why folks don't know what a Depression is. Why, when I was young – "

"Now, Mr. Reeder," Mrs. Reeder interrupted, "Tag don't have time to listen to one of your stories."

"No, I gotta be goin'," I said, getting up. "Papa and them's waitin'."

J.W. grabbed his coat. "I'll go with you." He settled his cap on his head backwards, the way he always wore it. He slipped his bean flip around his neck. He was a deadly shot with that bean flip.

"Tag, tell your mama not to worry. I'll have something to eat time you all get here," Mrs. Reeder said.

"Taw-ig, you boys move out in the woods and the Yahoos'll getcha," Mr. Reeder called after us. "I'd put you sorry-lookin' boys to cutting wood, doing something useful." His cackle followed us into the yard.

The other boys were ready. J.W. and I clambered into the back of the green wagon. Albert clucked to the mules.

J.W. pulled out a sack of R.J.R. tobacco from the bib pocket of his overalls, rolled a smoke, and lit it.

I stared in envy. "How long you been smokin'?"

"Oh, since I was about eight, I reckon. You want one?"

"No, I'd better not. Papa'd git me." I thought privately smoking was probably why J.W. was so small.

A hundred yards south of the Reeders', we passed a sandy wagon road leading west. Albert pointed. "Clearing's that way, 'bout a mile."

We passed Felix Bailey's, then turned east at Alley Reeder's log house. Mr. Reeder's eldest son, Alley liked to hunt gold, spin tall tales, and roam the woods, too.

We reached Bohannon school. "Is that where you go?" I asked J.W.

He glanced at the school. "Yep, 'fraid so."

"Who's the teacher?"

"Charley Watson."

"You like him?"

"Not enough you can tell it."

I hoped I liked the teacher better than J.W. seemed to, for I'd probably get to go to school some if Papa didn't keep us kids too busy.

When we reached Hickerson Hill, Mama and the little kids huddled around a fire. Papa and Frank were trying to dig the truck out with a post.

Albert unhitched the wagon at the top of the hill. We

walked down with the mules. Papa threw the post aside.

"Albert, shore appreciate this."

"Tickled to do it."

Albert backed the mules up to the truck and Frank and Loren hitched the trace chains to it.

"Now, Albert," Loren warned, "old Babe might balk."

"Yeah, and if she does, I'll cold-cock that sister with a hickory chunk." He picked up a big stick.

Frank climbed into the truck. Albert cracked the lines. The mules dug into the blue clay. The truck didn't budge.

"Haw, there! Babe! Kate!" Albert smacked Babe with the stick. The mule jumped forward, startled. The trace chain snapped, barely missing Albert.

"Now, what're we going to do?" Papa fumed. "That trace chain ain't going to hold."

"It's a'right, Mr. Speer," Albert said. "I brought a log chain gist in case."

He unhooked the broken trace chain and Loren and Frank hooked the heavy log chain to the double-tree, then the front axle of the truck. Albert took up the reins again.

"A'right, Babe, Kate! Lay in there!"

The mules strained against their collars.

"Ever'body push!" Albert hollered.

We all got behind the truck. The truck creaked and inched forward. It came out of the ditch suddenly, slid a little, and settled into the ruts. The load had shifted, breaking a spring. The back end of the truck leaned to one side. Albert hauled the truck to the top of the hill, then followed us back to Reeders'.

It was four o'clock, when we got there. Everyone was cold, and Pete and Hazel were crying. I could smell something good cooking.

"Miz Speer," Mrs. Reeder called out, "You get them little uns in here, where it's warm. Supper's waiting."

Papa wanted to get on to the clearing, but knew everyone was hungry. "I reckon we can take time," he conceded.

By the time we finished eating, it was nearly dark.

"Now, Mr. Speer, it's too late for you people to go on over to that clearing today," Mrs. Reeder said. "Miz Speer's got them sick little uns and them girls. We'll make some pallets out on the floor tonight. You men and them boys can take that team over there tomorrow and put that tent up while Miz Speer and them little uns stay here, where it's warm."

Papa's big barrel-chest heaved in resignation. "Might as well. The day's shot anyways. We'll git an early start in the morning."

Mr. Reeder cackled. "Them boys of yourn git out in the woods and the Yahoos and painters'll git 'em."

Joe, Frank, and I helped Albert, Loren, and J.W. with their chores; Mama and Opal helped Mrs. Reeder and Pansy with the dishes. Papa and Mr. Reeder sat by the fire talking. When we got back to the house, Mr. Reeder was telling Papa about the time he found a cave down in the canyon towards Boggy Creek.

"It had a stack of gold bullion in it big as a rick of wood," Mr. Reeder declared, his black eyes gleaming.

"What happened to it?" Papa asked.

"I left it there to come home and git the wagon. I nivver could find that same canyon agin."

Papa eyed him skeptically. Most of Mr. Reeder's gold stories ended this way.

Albert built a fire in the fireplace in the east room, across the dog trot. The room had two iron beds in it, a willow settee, a rocker, and Albert's new Victrola. We boys played some Jimmy Rodgers records, popped corn, and parched some peanuts in a bread pan. Loren played his French harp, and Albert his guitar, invariably starting off with *Wildwood Flower*.

"Many girls to go with around here?" Frank asked.

"A few," Albert replied. "Leota Ritter for one."

Frank grinned. One time, when visiting Uncle Bryan, he had taken Leota to church.

"Frank would get married if he could," I teased.

"Loren'll go with the girls," J.W. said, "if he's got someone to walk home with. He's afraid of the dark."

Loren took a swat at him. "Now, look out, Mr. Smarty. I'm not either."

J.W. persisted. "You're afraid even to go out to pee at night."

Loren turned red. "Look who's talkin'. Now that you mentioned it, you pee the bed!"

J.W. pounced on him. "That's one you could have kept from tellin'." A scuffle ensued.

Albert separated them. "You peckerwoods, knock it off. It's them Yahoos Loren's 'fraid of."

"What's Yahoos?" I asked.

"Aw, Papa's always trying to scare us, says there's Yahoos and panthers in the woods."

"Our papa don't like scarin' kids," Frank said.

"Well, Papa don't scare me much with his tales," Albert boasted.

"Oh, yeah?" Loren challenged. "What about them lights over in the meadow? Even you're afraid to go over there."

"What lights?" Joe asked, curious.

Loren spoke in a hushed tone. "We see them ever' summer, off to the south. A soft, round glow movin' through the trees."

"Probably the moon," I scoffed.

"Ain't no moon to the south," J.W. reminded.

I felt the hair tingle on the back of my neck. "What do you think it is?"

"Peat hacker's Nance," Loren whispered hoarsely.

"The ghost of an old Irish woman who onct lived over there in the trees," Albert explained. "Her husband was a peat hacker from the bogs of Ireland. One night, he murdered her. Poisoned her on castor beans. Papa says that light's her ghost over there, wanderin' around lost, huntin' him."

"Aw, there ain't no such thing as ghosts," Joe scoffed.

"Well, think what you want," Loren said. "But I've seen it. I shore ain't goin' out in the dark, not even to pee."

"Me neither," J.W. agreed.

I stared at them. Papa had always taught us not to be afraid of the dark and ghosts and things. "You're a bunch of 'fraidy cats," I taunted. "You don't scare me." I headed for the door to prove it.

"Tag, you better watch out," J.W. warned with a look of apprehension on his face.

I laughed and stepped outside into the dark. The others crowded onto the dog trot. I went towards the orchards, whistling to let them know I wasn't scared. I unbuttoned my fly. To the south, a low line of trees stood against the starry horizon. I thought I saw movement there. Something darted in the grass, startling me. An owl screeched. I hurried back to the house.

J.W. whooped. "What's the matter? Somethin' about to get you?"

"No," I denied, heart still pounding.

He grinned. "Then how come your pants are wet?"

I glanced down and my cheeks grew hot in embarrassment.

I slept beside J.W. on a pallet before the fire that night. I dreamed about the Yahoos and panthers chasing me. When I awoke, daylight barely lit the room, and Mr. Reeder's bent, grasshopper frame peered in from the doorway.

"Git up, you sorry looking Petes. You're about the biggest bunch of no-account boys I ever seed. Sunday or no, it's time to git to work. Breakfast's waitin'."

Frank, Joe, and I dressed quickly. We knew Papa

would be raring to go. When we got to the table everyone was there but little Pete. Mrs. Reeder asked Papa to return thanks. Just as he started, he glanced at the doorway and stopped to stare.

We all turned to look.

There stood Pete, his face and arms covered with measles.

Papa snorted. "Now, ain't this a purty come off?"

Chapter 5

THE CLEARING

None of us kids except Frank and Joe had ever had the measles. Even so, Mrs. Reeder would not hear of Mama taking Pete and Hazel over to the clearing.

"Miz Speer, you take them little uns over there in that cold, you're apt to drive the measles in and kill them kids. 'Sides, mine's already exposed. You just stay here a few days, where 'tis nice and warm. Them men and boys can go and put up that tent."

"I don't see how I can move 'em," Mama agreed, sighing in relief.

Papa's brow furrowed. He never liked putting anyone out, especially now with living so hard for everyone. "We'll git that tent up and git outa your way soon as possible."

When the chores were done, Frank, Papa, Mr. Reeder, Albert, Loren, and Joe went over to the clearing in the wagon. Ordinarily, Papa wouldn't work on Sunday but now "the ox is in the ditch," as he put it Biblically. Today, he meant to clear a site for the tent, level the ground, and dig a drain ditch.

Papa let me off for the day. J.W. and I went rabbit hunting. J.W. got two cottontails with his bean flip.

The next day, Papa meant to put the tent up, but we awoke to rain. "If it ain't one John Brown thing, it's another," Papa fumed. "We got a thousand and one things to do over there before planting time."

"Now, Mr. Speer," Mrs. Reeder scolded, "there ain't no use you fussing. The rain'll quit. When it does, you'll have plenty of time."

The rain continued that day and the next. There wasn't much to do, but listen to Mr. Reeder talk about hunting gold. J.W. made me a bean flip out of a forked hickory stick. I wasn't much good with it. About noon each day, the mail carrier, Tommy George, came by in his old brown Plymouth. We read the *Holdenville Daily*, *Weekly Kansas City Star*, and *Grit*.

Papa could hardly sit still. Every few minutes, he'd walk out on the front porch and look at the sky, anxious to get to work.

Wednesday, March first, the sun came out. It was too wet to work on the clearing. Papa and Mr. Reeder decided to take the wagon to Stuart, nine miles away. Bud and Eunice had sent Papa two dollars. He wanted some Old Hillside tobacco and a few groceries.

Albert was working on a willow settee. Frank stayed to help him. Joe, Loren, J.W., and I went hunting. Mrs. Reeder had kept her kids home from school so they wouldn't expose the rest of the school. This suited J.W. fine. He called his little feist. The dog trotted obediently at his heels.

"I wish I had a dog," I spoke wistfully.

"Why don't you git one?" J.W. asked.

"No, Papa won't let me. Once in Tulsa, I brought one home. Papa made me take it back, said I didn't need one. I sure did want it though."

We circled west through Mossy Hollow, hunting "long-eared rabbits," meaning squirrels out of season.

Papa and Mr. Reeder got back at sundown. Papa called, "Tag, come look in the wagon at what I got."

I ran to the wagon. In the bottom squirmed a black and tan hound, about four-weeks-old.

I couldn't believe my eyes. "A puppy! But you said we couldn't have a dog!"

"That was in town," Papa said. "We didn't need one then. Now, we do. She'll be a good hunting dog. Her mama's a bloodhound over at the State Penitentiary at McAlester."

I stared in awe at the pup. "What's her name?"

"Don't have one yet."

I hugged the pup. Her warm fur felt soft and smelled good. She had slick black hair, with golden beads over her eyes, long ears, and big lips that hung in folds. I thought she was the prettiest pup I'd ever seen. "How about naming her March," I suggested. "This is the first day of March."

So, March she became. Someday, she would help provide us with food, but for the moment, she was all a boy's heart could desire.

Next morning, Papa and the older boys went to the clearing to put up the tent. J.W. and I stayed behind to play with the pup. On Friday, Papa and the others got the truck unloaded and things in the tent. That night, a strong wind came up. The other boys weren't feeling too well next morning. When I went with Joe, Papa, and Frank, we found two of the tent stakes pulled out. The canvas sagged against the furniture.

"Dog tick it!" Papa fussed. "I was afraid she'd blow down in that wet ground."

"Papa, I'm not shore it did." Frank showed us one of the stakes. The rope looked as if it had been deliberately untied.

Puzzled, Papa shook his big head. "Who you reckon would want to do that?" He gazed at the log cabin. Papa had asked Mr. Peace to move, but he hadn't yet.

Frank followed his gaze. "You think it was Mr. Peace?"

"No cause to. No, it must have been the wind." Papa seemed unwilling to think otherwise.

He sent me back to Mr. Reeder's for a pair of posthole diggers. He, Frank, and Joe chopped some small logs in the woods. We dug a trench around the tent with the posthole diggers, laid the logs in the trench, and tied the tent ropes to the logs. We covered the logs and banked the dirt around the tent.

"There, that ought to hold it," Papa said.

He worried about leaving our stuff there unprotected.

"Joe and me'll stay tonight," Frank volunteered.

"I'll take turns with you 'til the family gets here," Papa agreed.

Next day, Sunday, all the other kids broke out with the measles but me. Mama said I must be too ornery to catch them. She and Mrs. Reeder scurried from one to the other with aspirin. I peeked in at J.W.

"You lucky stiff," he spoke weakly.

"You sorry-looking Pete," I returned.

He grinned. "At least I don't have to go to school."

We spent another week at the Reeders'. Each morning, Papa, Frank, Joe, and I got up at daylight, and did the chores for the Reeders. We drove the wagon to the clearing. We piled brush, dragged logs, carried rocks, pulled stumps, and burned weeds, getting the land ready to plow.

I liked the clearing already. It lay at the end of a wagon trail a mile from the main sandy road. The trail curved around a small canyon. Oak and blackjack filled the canyon. A single pine stood at the edge of the canyon. Each time we passed the lonesome pine, Frank broke into song:

"Oh, they cut down that old, pine tree,
And hauled it away to the mill,
To make a coffin of pine,
For that sweetheart of mine,
When they cut down that old, pine tree."

His haunting words seemed to fit the surroundings.

The bean-shaped clearing, consisting of seven or eight acres, sat on a ridge. The land around it was open range. The clearing had a brush fence to protect it from the grazing livestock. Many deadened trees and stumps still stood in the clearing. The two log cribs stood at the north end of the clearing, and our tent sat near the back, beneath a tall hickory.

Pine Spring lay in a shady glen, about a quarter-mile behind the tent, down a steep, rutted path. The cold water bubbled up in a sandstone bowl between two tall rocks. Papa cherished that spring. To him water was a symbol of spiritual and material value. He believed all life began with water. Without it, nothing could live. He liked to fish and to have a cold drink after a hard day's work.

Pine Spring fed into a branch that flowed into Piney Creek at the foot of the ridge, then into Boggy Creek. South of the clearing, the ridge dropped sharply into Mossy Hollow. Blackjacks, red oak, post oak, and hickory covered the sandstone hills. Squirrels, bluejays, opossum, rabbits, and skunks lived in the woods. Papa and the rest of the family always called the clearing "Pine Spring." Uncle Bryan called it "Starvation Hill." Frank and I called it a "Hillback To Boggy." Whatever the name, the clearing was a new way of life for us.

Papa teemed with impatience to get all the work done on the clearing. The wind had blown over many of the deadened trees. Cattle had pushed in the brush fence in several places. The wagon road led through the clearing, which had a wire gate at each side. Our neighbors Buford McNutt, Ted Hickerson, and Evan Vaughn used the road to haul water from Pine Springs, when their own supply ran low. Papa closed the gates and made a new road around the clearing. We cleaned out the spring.

Buford McNutt's boys, Harold and Sanford, got angry

because they had to drive their wagon around the clearing to reach the spring.

Papa told them, "This my place now. I'm aimin' to farm it. I can't have ever'body drivin' back and forth 'crost it."

That evening, I found a dead rabbit in the spring. "It's been shot," I told Papa. "I betcha it was them McNutt boys. You goin' to git them, Papa?"

He shook his head. "Wouldn't do no good. Can't prove it. Some people gist let their kids run wild."

Papa borrowed a Georgia stock from Mr. Reeder and laid off the land in rows. His face lit at the smell of the moist, brown earth.

"Man is born to the land and water," he said. "On the land a man can earn his bread by the sweat of his brow." He gripped the plow handles and sang:

Oh, I will shout and I will sing,
When the redeemed are gathered in . . ."

Bud and Eunice sent two more dollars and the Sunday comics from Tulsa. Papa went to Stuart and bought seed potatoes, cabbage plants, English peas, two gallons of onion sets, cucumber seeds, beets, carrots, radishes. Mr. Reeder gave him a bushel of seed corn to shell and plant. As the ground began to warm, Papa became even more impatient to move the family to the clearing and to start planting.

Opal balked. "I ain't movin' to the woods."

"Ain't movin', your hindleg," Papa said. "Where do you think you're goin'?"

"I'm stayin' here with Mrs. Reeder until Vesta and Virgil come down. Then I'm goin' back to Tulsa and live with them."

"Now, Opal," Papa argued, "you can't do that. Virgil has his own family to support and they's barely gittin' by as it is."

Opal burst into tears. When the time came to move back into the tent, she had no choice. "We'll never have a nice house again," she sobbed.

"Opal," Mama soothed, "when Mr. Peace leaves, maybe we can move into the cabin."

All his life, it seemed to me that Papa was struggling and finagling just to live. So it was now in order to obtain the tools we needed to farm the land. He walked seven miles to see George Bishop, who gave him some hoes. The hoes were without handles and worn down to about two inches wide. Papa sharpened the hoes with a rusty file, and cut a hickory handle for each.

One day, he found a rusty, double-bitted axe head in the road. He soaked the axe head in coal-oil and cleaned it with sandrock. He made a handle for the axe, shaping and fitting the wood with a drawing knife, and smoothing it with a piece of broken glass. He sharpened the axe on Mr. Reeder's grindstone.

Leota Ritter's father sent him a cross-cut saw, the teeth worn smooth as an old hound's. Papa sharpened the teeth, and knocked some "set" into the blade with a hammer. He sanded the saw, and greased it with a meat skin, then cut two handles and tied them on with bailing wire.

With these crude tools, we commenced to dig out a living. Papa laid out the garden. We cut seed potatoes and planted them, along with peas, onions, and corn. Mrs. Reeder gave us a sack of whipporwill peas to eat. We planted some of those. Papa got some tobacco seed from Mr. Reeder and made a tobacco bed.

Papa gazed at the straight furrows in satisfaction. "If a man knows how to work, he won't starve."

March got in everyone's way as we worked. Papa fussed at her.

"Now you got to learn to stay outa Papa's way," I scolded the pup. "Stay back here and mind."

We cut stove wood and traded a rick to John Overton

for a dozen eggs. We traded two ricks to Mr. Ritter for a dollar. Papa chased a rabbit into a hollow log and chopped it out to save shotgun shells, which cost two cents apiece.

"If we can gist make it through March," Papa kept saying, "we can make it the rest of the year."

We hoed the ground and planted beans, okra, and squash. Once a day, Joe and I walked around the brush fence, checking for holes, where the cattle might get in.

One evening, a tall man driving a team of mules, stopped us at the gate. He had a paunchy belly, thin, sandy hair, and stubbly cheeks. His small, green eyes glared at us. "What're you people doin' in here?" he asked.

"Farmin'," Joe replied.

The man's glance slid away. "You got no right in here. This is open rangeland. Who said you could live here?"

"Papa traded for the right with Albert Reeder."

"Albert Reeder had no right." The man talked fast and would not look directly at us. "No son-of-a-bitch does. You people better stay out of the damn woods or you'll wish you had."

He drove off at a rapid clip. Joe and I hurried to the tent to tell Papa. He didn't know who the man was. Next morning, Papa asked Loren and Albert Reeder about him.

"Sounds like Lem Hatcher,"* Albert said. "Lives two miles west in the bottoms on Boggy Creek. Runs cattle, and some say he makes corn whiskey. He wanted the clearin'. It's new ground and would make good corn land. But I beat him to it."

"Hatcher don't git along with nobody but the Looney boys, Mott Poe, and the Kimes boys," Loren added. "They're all a sorry, tough bunch."

---

*Name changed.

"Aw, Hatcher's own family's a'right," Albert said. "He's a hard worker, but ever'body decent is suspicious of that peckerwood."

"Why?" Papa wanted to know.

"Been known to steal," Loren said. "Go out and shoot somebody else's hog, when he wants meat. Plumb full of general orneriness."

"Alley says Lem's got a still down in the woods," Albert warned. "He don't want nobody foolin' around there. You better keep an eye on that gentleman."

Papa's chin, beneath its stubbly, black beard, set firmly. "Ain't nobody goin' to run me off here. This is all I got, and I got to feed my family."

We saw nothing more of Lem Hatcher the next few days, but I could not forget his cold, green eyes. He lived near Mott Poe, whose nephew, Matthew Kimes, was in the McAlester Penitentiary for killing twenty-two men.

The garden shot up. Mr. Peace moved out, going to "R'zony" and make "willar cheers."

The family hurried over to the cabin to see if we could move in. The smell reached us before we got there. Trash littered the dirt floor. Boards covered the glass-less windows. It was obvious the Peace family had used one corner of the cabin for a toilet during bad weather.

Mama covered her nose from the stench. "They were living like animals!"

Papa shook his head in disgust. "Larie, I don't think we can use this for anything but a pig pen or barn."

Opal looked stricken. "We won't have a house."

"I'll build you a cabin someday," Papa promised. "Soon as I git time."

This was not enough for Opal. She ran off into the woods, crying.

We burned the trash and throwed some fresh dirt in the cabin. Frank and I gagged at the smell.

We burned some fallen trees in the center of the clearing that day. The wind blew out of the south. The log pile still smouldered at dark. We watched the glowing embers as we ate supper.

Suddenly, Papa stiffened. Flames blazed in the brush fence at the south end of the clearing. Sparks, carried on the wind, threatened the whole fence, and fire swept towards the tent.

"Fire!" Papa jumped up and seized his old T-Barker, double-barreled shotgun. "Ever'body grab a wet tow-sack or something! We gotta git up there and stop it or it'll burn us out."

Chapter 6

NEAR STARVATION

We scrambled from the tent. Mama snatched up some old blankets, a jacket, and a pair of overalls for us to use in beating out the flames. We got the hoes. Frank grabbed the axe as we ran towards the fire.

Papa slammed two shells into the shotgun. "That son-of-a-bitch! If I catch him up there settin' that fence, I'll fill him full of number six shot!"

I didn't have time to wonder what Papa meant by that right then. The fire was swooshing through the dry brush we had piled on the fence. Glowing embers sailed on the wind, starting new fires farther down. Smoke stung my eyes. I could feel the blistering heat as we tore at the fence with the hoes and axe. Mama and the girls tried to beat out the flames with the quilts and clothes. The fire kept spreading.

Papa dropped back. "We ain't goin' to do it this way! Move down! Tear part of the fence out! Make a break in it!"

We rushed ahead of the raging fire. We jerked the jagged branches from the fence and tossed them aside, making a hole in the fence. The fire caught up with us and jumped the gap.

Papa waved. "Farther down! Move farther down!"

We raced downwind again and tore anew at the fence.

The fire spread into the dry grass, threatening the woods. Papa leaped the fence and fought the flames with the pair of overalls. A red ember landed in a patch of dry grass near the tent.

"Look!" I shouted, pointing.

Flames spread rapidly toward the tent. For a moment we stood frozen, all knowing the paraffin, which Papa had melted in kerosene and spread on the tent to waterproof it, would catch the tent afire easily.

Pete stood before the tent, naked and clutching his coveralls. Mama had been getting him ready for bed, when the fire broke out. He ran to the flames, and flogged them with his coveralls.

"Cuss 'em! Cuss 'em!" he hollered.

Mama screamed and raced towards Pete. By the time she got there, he had the flames snuffed out. Mama clutched his naked body to her, and sobbed in relief. Pete gazed in dismay at his scorched coveralls and fell over bawling.

The rest of us turned back to the fire and fought it with new vigor. The fire approached the gap again. This time the break held. The fire gave a final, ferocious roar, then sank to the ground with a sigh. We threw dirt on the glowing embers.

We gathered by the charred fence, still shaken, our faces and clothes black streaked, and hair singed. March crept out of the shadows, belly close to the ground.

Papa flung down the overalls, which he had used to beat out the flames, and picked up his shotgun. "If I ever find out who that son-of-a-bitch was, I'll shoot him here and now!"

Frank frowned in puzzlement. "Papa, how do you know it was someone? We was burnin' logs – "

"They's no way," Papa interrupted, glowering fiercely, "that fire could have spread from the north end to the south end of this clearing with the wind blowing from the south." He let his meaning sink in. "I thought, when I ran up here, I heard someone rattlin' in the brush, but I didn't have time to go and see. I'm goin' to take a look around now. You boys stay here and keep watch. Don't let that fire start up again."

He melted into the dark beyond the brush fence. The girls headed for the tent. Joe, Frank, and I hunkered in the dirt, watching the hot coals.

"Frank, you reckon Papa would kill somebody?" The idea seemed foreign to me, Papa being so religious and all.

Frank shook his head. "I don't know. He was awful mad, and a person'll do lots of things when threatened."

We fell silent, straining to catch any sounds in the night. After awhile, Papa came back, his face still grim.

"Can't tell nothin' tonight. We'll take another look in the mornin'. Frank, we'll keep watch tonight."

Frank nodded.

I started for the tent then turned back. "Papa, who do you think it was? Lem Hatcher?"

Papa's mouth set in a thin line. "If it was, it'd better be the last time he tries it."

The rest of the night passed uneventful. Next morning, Joe, Frank, and I followed Papa down to where the fire had begun. Papa searched the ground, then squatted above a set of hobnailed footprints and several burned matches.

"It was set a'right," he said.

Frank looked disturbed. "What'cha goin' to do about it?"

Papa's eyes glittered. "I'll let 'em know."

Later, Alley Reeder appeared as if out of nowhere. He was a tall, thin man with a thick, black beard. He roamed the woods, silent as an Indian. He often disappeared in the woods for three or four days. He knew everything that went on in the woods. Not even the dogs would bark at him.

Alley looked around and observed casually, "Had a fire here last night."

Papa nodded. "Yeah, I figger it was set."

Alley's black eyes hooded. "Got any idee?"

"No," Papa snapped, "but if you know anybody that's got any notion about burnin' us out, you better tell 'em if I ever find 'em settin' fire to my fence again, I'll drop 'em right there. This is my life and my kids' life. This is all we've got, and I aim to protect it."

Alley studied him a moment, then slipped back into the woods as silently as he had come.

He must have got word to somebody because we had no more trouble with fence burning. We set about rebuilding the fence. When done, we returned to our work in the garden.

Spring seemed a long time in coming. The weather turned cold and rainy. The sack of whipporwill peas was about gone. We searched the woods for poke salad, sour dock, and lamb's quarter. We hunted for rabbits and squirrels, but they were becoming scarce, what with everyone hunting them. Papa was saving his two brass shells for an emergency. He showed us how to run a rabbit into a hollow log and chop him out, or "rock" a squirrel. He taught us how to set bird traps made out of sticks and how to build rabbit gums.

He showed me how to fish with some old hooks and blue butchershop cord tied onto the end of willow poles. He found a wasp nest in the woods, broke it open, and raked out the tender, white larva.

"Perch bait," he said with a toothless grin.

We went down to Piney Creek. He showed me where the perch liked to lie in deep, eddy pools against the banks, among the roots and brush in the water. Sometimes we dug for red worms and caught catfish in Boggy Creek. Like the squirrels and rabbits, the fish were getting scarce; without them, our bellies grew lankier.

Uncle Bryan and Aunt Eula came to see us. "We'd

been here sooner," Uncle Bryan apologized, "but the young uns tuk down with the measles."

Mama grinned. "Yeah, I 'spect so."

Uncle Bryan and Aunt Eula left us a little more flour and a pound sack of Silver Bell coffee. These went fast.

One day, a flock of turtle doves settled on a tree in the clearing. Papa trained his shotgun on the doves.

Frank said, "Papa, you'll git in trouble. They's not in season."

"They are now." Papa squeezed the trigger. Five doves tumbled to the ground. Mama stewed them and made dumplings.

The next day, when I went to the mailbox, I met J.W. Reeder. He killed a chicken hawk with his bean flip. I took the hawk home and we ate it.

Papa didn't always pray before meals, but sometimes after supper, he would give a long discourse on the Bible. "You got to have faith in the Lord," he would say. "You got to believe and He'll provide. He promises the little sparrows a livin', too, but He expects 'em to git out there and scratch for it."

I always escaped from his preaching as soon as I could. I wasn't certain about Papa's God. It seemed to me any God who needed constant praise must be insecure. Also, if everyone got what they prayed for, that would upset the natural laws of nature.

April moved along with mild and sunny days. The dogwood and redbuds burst into bloom. The cardinals and bluebirds sang all day. At night, the owls, mocking birds, and whipporwills took over. With the warm weather, Mama and Opal washed down by the spring.

Papa continued to show us kids how to hunt and live in the woods. One day, while we were hoeing the beans, Papa lifted his head. "Someone's comin'."

I heard nothing. "How do you know?"

"Learn to listen and you can tell things. Right now, the birds have stopped singin'."

He was right. A moment later, I saw Alley Reeder slipping through the woods.

Next day, two bluejays commenced screaming in the woods. Papa listened. "A squirrel or somethin' is invadin' their territory."

"How can you tell?" I asked. His sense of the woods still amazed me.

"By the sound of it."

The scolding in the woods increased.

"He's gittin' close to 'em." Papa dropped his hoe and picked up the axe. "Come on, let's see if we can find that squirrel."

We kids ran after him. March kept getting under Papa's feet. I called her back, fearful he would get angry.

"Let her run," Papa said. "She's smellin' the woods and squirrels. She'll learn that way."

We plunged through the brush and trees after Papa. I wondered how he'd find the squirrel.

"Spread out," Papa said. "The best place to find him this time of year is where he can git somethin' to eat. Look for a big hickory tree with young nuts on it. He'll be cuttin' and droppin' 'em to the ground."

We fanned out.

"Here he is!" Betty hollered. "Sure 'nuff, here he is!"

We ran to see. Papa grunted. "Yep, there he sits."

The squirrel sat high among the branches of the tall tree.

"Frank," Papa said, "git on the other side. He'll turn tree on us and git away if he can."

Papa chunked a rock at the squirrel. The squirrel slid around the tree. Frank threw another rock from the opposite side. The squirrel jumped into a small blackjack tree and disappeared into a hole.

Papa grinned. "We got him now. Tag, climb up there and stop up that hole."

I skinned up the tree, and not having anything else to use, stuffed my shirt into the opening.

Papa chopped the tree down, then cut a notch in it, two feet above the hole. He felt inside the tree with a stick. I could hear the squirrel moving inside. Papa trapped the squirrel in the bottom of the cavity with the stick. He cut another notch in the tree beside the squirrel.

I could see the squirrel inside now. "How we goin' to git him out?"

"You'll see." Papa sharpened a stick. He rammed the stick through the hole and pierced the squirrel just behind the head. The squirrel shrieked, and goose-bumps pricked my arms. The girls turned pale and moved back.

Papa spoke without emotion. "It's the way you got to do, when you don't have any shells."

He waited until the squirrel ceased squealing, then cut the hole bigger, and snatched out the squirrel. He finished it off with a quick rap on the head. March danced around, yapping in excitement. Papa let her smell the squirrel, and she licked the fur.

Papa petted her. "She's goin' to make a fine squirrel dog."

We returned to the clearing. Papa showed us boys how to skin the squirrel, holding it up by the hindlegs, cutting the skin at the backbone, and working the skin down. He threw the entrails to March, who snatched them up and ran off to the woods growling. I carried the squirrel to Mama.

She clapped her hands together. "Lord-a-mercy, I guess the Lord does answer prayer."

This time of year, the rabbits seemed somewhat tame. Sometimes, I tried to catch them, but they always hopped away. "How come they always see me?" I asked Papa.

"Well," he replied, "nature has a way of providin' ever'-thing with a way of protectin' itself. The skunk has a bad smell; a squirrel can climb and jump; a fish can swim. A rabbit's natural means of protectin' itself is that he never bats his eyes. Gist be real still until you git close to him, then throw a rock."

Papa taught us to look for rabbit droppings to locate the rabbit's habitat. He would not let us eat the older rabbits this time of year. "You have to be careful of rabbit warts," he said. Nor would he let us eat the female rabbits. "They have young uns somewhere."

Once, I saw a mother rabbit limping across the hoed ground. "She's crippled!" I dropped my hoe and took after her. She zig-zagged, staying just ahead of me and bleating in a pitiful voice.

"Might as well come back," Papa called. "You're chasin' the wrong thing."

I halted, panting and wondering what he meant.

Papa searched the ground, where the rabbit had jumped up. "She's got a nest around here. She was gist pretendin' to be crippled to lure you away from 'em. Birds'll do that, too." He found the nest of half-grown rabbits next to a log. "Let 'em grow for awhile. They'll make more meat thata way."

The few rabbits and squirrels we could find were not enough to keep us going now. Mrs. Reeder's whippor-will peas played out. We ranged farther, hunting greens and small game. The fat melted off me. Pete whined all the time in hunger.

Papa strode across the garden each morning, as if trying to hurry it. "If we can gist make it to the first of May," he would say, "the garden'll be ready to eat on."

One morning, he pulled out his black coin purse and handed me his last dime. "Tag, go to Rock Creek store. Get a jug of coal-oil. That'll be a nickel. Take four more cents and git me two shotgun shells. A-body never knows when he might need 'em around here. Bring me back the other penny."

I pocketed the dime, and set out down the road, bare-footed. Birds whistled in the woods and ants and bugs crawled in the dust. The store was two and a half miles away, next to Rock Creek school. I bought the coal-oil and shells and started back. A team of mules and wagon rattled up behind me.

"Wanta ride?" Earl Lane asked.

I climbed into the wagon, grateful. Earl Lane was a large man with black hair, heavy beard, and long nose. He lived in a nice home a mile north of the Reeders with his mother and old maid sister.

"You one of that bunch livin' over at Pine Spring?" he asked.

I nodded.

"Findin' many squirrels to eat?"

I shook my head. "Not many." I took his measure. He looked prosperous enough. "Say, you got any work you want done?" I asked on impulse.

"Well, I might have. I need some posts cut."

I didn't care for that kind of hard work, but the thought of something good to eat spurred me on. "We'll do it."

Earl Lane glanced at me. "Now, I can't pay cash."

"That's a'right." My enthusiasm was only slightly dampened. "We'll take anything good to eat."

"All I got to offer is some whipporwill peas."

My spirits sank. By now, I had my fill of those. "Ain't you got any meat? Any butterbeans? Not even any blackeyed peas?"

Earl Lane shook his head. "You still want the job?"

I nodded, though thoroughly disheartened.

I told Papa about the posts. Next day, he, Joe, Frank, and I split out a hundred posts for Earl Lane in exchange for a hundred pounds of whipporwill peas.

During the next few weeks, Mama tried every way she could to make the peas tasty. She mashed some and mixed them with sage, and fried them in patties. Papa shot another rabbit and ground the rabbit up with some of the peas to make "rabbit sausage." We ate boiled peas, cold peas, hot peas, morning, noon, and night. The whipporwill peas kept us alive, but soon, none of us could stand the taste of them.

Opal and Betty took sick from eating the poor food. Hazel and I came down with the chills from the spring water. Pete cried all the time. Mama's thin frame looked shrunken as she moved about, trying to tend to everyone. Papa spent a lot of time in the woods praying.

Then one morning, the whipporwill peas gave out again. We had nothing left to eat.

Frightened, Mama tried to hush Pete. "This baby needs milk," she said.

Papa's brow beetled. "I know it. Them other kids need quinine." He sat silent at the barren table, his face grim. Abruptly, he stood and reached for his shotgun and slipped his last shell into it.

Mama read the desperate look in his eyes. "Henry, what're you goin' to do?"

He stalked to the door of the tent. "I don't know. I've thought about it. I've prayed, I've worked hard. Nothin' helps." Tears filled his eyes. "I'm going to town and try to git some credit. I'm going to try to do what's right. If I can't -- well, one way or another -- when I come home, my kids are goin' to have somethin' to eat."

Mama clutched the back of a scarred chair. "Henry, I wouldn't take that gun."

His mouth tightened. "Yeah, you never know what might happen."

He motioned to Frank. They left the tent. We heard the old truck start up and clatter from the clearing. Mama stood frozen. I had never seen her looking so scared.

Chapter 7

SPRING AT LAST

Silence hung in the tent long after the old truck sputtered from the clearing. Mama slumped in a chair.

Finally, Opal spoke in a scared whisper, "Mama? What if Papa robs somebody and they send him to the pen? What'll happen to us?"

Mama shook her head, too numb to speak.

Joe moved towards the tent flap.

"Where you goin'?" I asked.

"Reckon I might as well hoe the 'taters. Papa won't like it if he comes home and no work's been done."

I dragged myself from bed, still shaking with the chills. "Might as well go with you."

"You ought to stay in bed."

"Maybe I'll feel better movin' around in the sun." Truth was, I couldn't bear seeing Mama's expression. Besides, time would pass faster if I was busy, and maybe I wouldn't think so much about being hungry.

Joe and I moved slowly up and down the rows, chopping weeds. Joe was a lot like Papa. He liked the land and hoped to be a farmer someday.

"Joe," I said, "do you reckon Papa actually would rob a fellar? Maybe hold up a grocery store?"

Joe paused. "Naw, I don't 'magine he'd go that far. After all, the old man's a purty good Christian, when you git right down to it. Still -- " He shrugged and lapsed into silence.

We worked the potatoes and started on the beans though they had been worked two days before. May set fair upon the land. Birds hollered and rabbits hopped in the brush as if nothing unusual was taking place.

At noon, Joe and I went to the tent to get a drink. Mama had nothing on the table for dinner. Her face still looked hurt and empty.

"You want us to go down to Miz Reeder's and borrow something to eat?" Joe asked.

"No," Mama said. "We've borrowed enough already."

Joe and I went back to work. All afternoon we kept watch for the old truck. I wondered what we would do if Papa robbed a store and got sent to prison. Would the law get Frank, too? How could Joe and I manage without Papa and Frank?

About four o'clock, Joe laid down his hoe. "Think I'll go hunt some lamb's quarter along the road."

I went with him all the way to the mailbox. The main road lay empty as far as we could see.

I voiced my deepest fear: "Papa must be in jail."

Joe refused to give up. "It's a long ways to town."

We walked home, finding a few greens on the way.

Mama accepted them gratefully. "Don't look like enough for all of us."

"That's a'right. Give 'em to the sick ones. I'm not very hungry," Joe lied.

He and I went back outside. Evening had come. Jar-flies hummed. In the distance, we could hear Alley Reeder's wife calling the cows: "Soo-oo-uk! Soo-oo-uk!"

Joe drew a deep breath. "I guess you're right, he must be in jail."

I knew he had given up on Papa, too. Joe hurried towards the woods, trying to hide his tears. March began to bark. I saw headlights bouncing up the wagon road.

"Joe, wait!" I called. "I hear somebody comin'!"

He turned, his face pale. "Must be the sheriff."

Mama and the others gathered outside the tent in a fearful knot. The headlights stopped at the gate. Someone got out to open it, and his dark figure sliced the light beams.

"It's Papa!" I shouted in joy.

In a few minutes, the truck was at the tent. Papa and Frank each carried in a big box of groceries.

Papa grinned. "We got somethin' to eat."

He unpacked the groceries: A slab of sidemeat, baking powder, soda, potatoes, sorghum molasses, crackers, cornmeal, canned milk, fifty-pound sack of flour, beans, dried prunes, shotgun shells, graham crackers, quinine, even some tobacco for Papa and a tin of snuff for Mama. I couldn't believe it!

Mama still looked fearful. "Henry — there must be three — four dollars worth of stuff here — how'd you— "

"It's a'right, Larie," Papa interrupted. "I got some credit."

"Glory be!" Mama sank into a chair and burst into tears of relief.

Papa tried to console her. As soon as everything settled down, Mama fried some sidemeat and potatoes. She made biscuits and thickening gravy. We ate our fill. Replete, we settled back to hear what had happened.

Papa was a natural-born story teller. He took his time, lighting his pipe. He looked relaxed, the first time in a long time, and began.

When Papa and Frank got to town, there weren't too many people on the street. A couple of teams stood before Adams' drugstore, and an old man sat on a bench before the hotel. Papa told Frank to pull up before Claude World's grocery store.

Papa left the gun in the truck and walked into the store. He asked Mr. World if he could give him a little credit. Mr. World said no, he had too many on credit now. Papa told him how hard up he was and his kids were starving. He could pay come summer when he got a little work. He had always been an honest man and paid his debts. Mr. World still said no. Frank and Papa went back to the truck.

Papa got the gun. They went into Bates Bruce's General Store. Two or three men sat around talking. Papa asked Mr. Bruce if he could have a little credit. Mr. Bruce said he didn't know him. How did he know he wasn't just passing through the country? Papa told him he had lived here twelve years ago. Mr. Bruce said that was before he opened his business here. Papa told him to ask anybody that knew him. Ask George Gould or "Arkansas Bob" Hall. They would tell him whether he paid his bills or not. Mr. Bruce still looked doubtful. Papa told him he would work, do anything to keep his kids from starving. He eased the shotgun into his arms. Mr. Bruce didn't say nothing, just stared at it.

One of the men at the back of the room looked up. "By grab! Henry Speer!" It was Arkansas Bob Hall.

Mr. Bruce asked him: "You know this man?"

"By grab, I reckon I do."

"Will he pay his bills?"

"If he won't, he shore has changed since the last time I saw him. If he wants something on credit and this store was mine, I'd let him have anything he wants."

"That's good enough for me," Mr. Bruce said. "Get anything you need, Mr. Speer. Write it down."

Papa slapped his knee at the joy of remembering. "Then another man come up, Joe Romine," he continued. "He said, 'I remember you. I recollect you was always willin' to work and had some boys. If you got some boys that can work, I got some land that needs to be cleared. I can't pay much. No cash. But they can work out somethin' to eat."

"A cow," Frank added, "we're goin' to work out a cow."

Mama's thin hand rose to her lips in joy. "A cow?"

"Papa said Joe and I could work," Frank said. "Forty cents a day and board. The cow is twenty dollars."

"A cow," Mama repeated as if in a dream.

Papa knocked the ashes from his pipe. "Mr. Romine told me to come over Monday or Tuesday, and he would take me to Holdenville in his car. He knows a fellar there in charge of the WPA. He'll try to git me on."

I could see us back on easy street. "You shore was lucky, Papa."

He squinched his eyes and snorted. "Lucky your hindfoot! Arkansas Bob Hall told me he seldom goes to town. He gist happened to be there today. Gist when I needed him. Now I don't figger that was an accident."

I wondered if the Lord had provided after all.

Frank and Joe went to work for Mr. Romine early Monday morning. Mr. Romine, an old German, lived north of Rock Creek Store. He had an electric plant, tractor, and green disc-wheeled touring car. The harder times got, the easier it was for him to get someone to work for forty cents a day and room and board. He had two girls about Frank's age. Frank hated going over there, ragged and hair shaggy. Even so, he and Joe left before daylight to walk the four miles. They would return on Saturday afternoons for the weekend.

With the pressure off Papa to provide something to eat, I thought the work on the clearing might ease off a little. I didn't reckon right. Papa wasn't one to ease off, not with a bill hanging over his head.

He settled his big hat on his head and picked up the crosscut saw. "Tag, you and Opal git your riggin' on. I made a deal to cut a hundred posts for a penny apiece."

"A hundred posts," I groaned. "That's a lot of work."

He stabbed me with a piercing look. "You like to eat, don't you?"

With the quinine, I felt better. Opal still felt a little

weak. She went along without complaining. She wore a pair of Joe's overalls, a long-sleeved shirt, and one of Mama's sunbonnets. Big for her age, she worked patiently, seemingly resigned to what we were doing.

It took us two days to cut the posts. Papa caught a ride into Stuart and paid the dollar on his grocery bill.

Next morning, he walked over to Mr. Romine's to go to Holdenville. He left us kids plenty of work. He believed idle hands were the devil's workshop. When Papa got back, he had a WPA job as an overseer, building some bridges. That night, he told us how it happened.

He said Mr. Romine had some pull with Tom Anglin, a lawyer over at Holdenville, the county seat of Hughes County. Mr. Anglin had run for governor and had political connections. He took a liking to Papa. Papa was a strong Democrat and kept up on things. The job of overseer paid three dollars a day. It was only for two days a week, but we were happy about it.

Right from the start, though, Papa had trouble on the job. Some of the men were jealous of a stranger being put over them. They liked doing things their own way, instead of Papa's. He lived in a tent, and the others lived in houses.

Some of the trouble was Papa's own fault. He was talkative and argumentative. He believed in doing things one way. He made his politics and religion plain. Most of those in the community were Holiness. Papa was Baptist. He believed in the Second Coming and baptism. He did not believe in speaking in tongues. On first meeting, he came on as being loud, vociferous, and overbearing. Some of the men wanted him thrown off the job, but Papa was a good worker and knew what he was doing. He left before daylight each morning to walk to Rock Creek to work and got home after dark.

On the days Papa worked, the burden of the labor on the clearing fell on Opal, Betty, Hazel, and me.

One evening, I heard March barking and looked up to

see Joe. He came into the tent looking sheepish. "They sent me home," he said.

"Sent you home?" Papa echoed. "What for?"

Joe hung his head. "I peed the bed."

I could feel his humiliation. He had kidney trouble and sometimes an accident happened.

Though Papa was hard in some ways, in others he had feeling. "That's a'right. If it was somethin' you could help it would be different. I need you here anyway."

Joe looked grateful. "Mr. Romine didn't exactly let me go. He said I could still walk back and forth to work."

Papa shook his head. "No, it wouldn't be worth it. I got plenty of work here for you. Forget it. Frank can keep on workin' for the cow."

During the next few weeks, life on the clearing settled into a ceaseless bustle. Papa wanted more land so we could plant some corn, peavines, and cane for the cow. We circled five more acres and started clearing the land. We piled the brush and rocks into a new fence.

Sometimes, Mama thought Papa was pushing us kids too hard. She helped us with the hoeing when we got behind. Mama was always busy, cooking, washing, pressing clothes for Frank and Joe to go to Saturday night community singing at Bohannon, or for Frank to go see Leota Ritter.

Pete tagged after the rest of us. He wanted to plant everything. Once, he planted Papa's hammer; a second time, a fork; a third time, two marbles.

Those May days were warm and golden. Papa continued to teach us kids about the woods: what things were good to eat; what was poison; how to make a tree fall where you wanted to; that moss grew on the north side of a tree; that post oak made the best fence posts; that red oak made good boards. One could boil red oak bark and use the juice in making a poultice to treat sores and wounds. We learned that sassafras tea was good for a person who had worms. Papa taught us the names of the wildflowers and birds. We learned about centipedes, stinging scorpions, and snakes. To me, a city kid, this was a great experience.

The garden came on. We had plenty of vegetables. Papa shot squirrels and doves. He got a bucket of lard, middling of meat, and some sorghum molasses from Mr. Romine. Mr. Romine subtracted these from Frank's wages.

We never worked on Sunday. *"The Lord created the Sabbath for man. On the Sabbath ye shall rest,"* Papa quoted.

Sometimes, Papa let us off early on Saturday. I didn't waste much time getting away from the clearing, afraid he'd change his mind. I liked to go to the woods by myself, and watch the birds and squirrels, or fish on Boggy or Piney.

One Saturday, when Papa let us off early, I asked if I could walk down to Uncle Bryan's to fish and stay all night. Papa said I could. I put on a clean pair of overalls and took off.

At Hickerson Hill, I met Uncle Bryan and his family in their wagon. They were going to Grandma McNutt's for the singing that night.

"Why don't you git in and go with us?" Aunt Eula said.

I hesitated, not knowing what to do.

"There'll be lots of kids your age and pies and cakes," she added.

I forgot the fishing and piled in the wagon with them.

We met others from the neighborhood going to Grandma McNutt's. The yard was full of wagons by the time we got there at sunset. I saw Frank and Joe.

"I didn't know you was a comin'!" I exclaimed.

"Heard about the singin' after you left," Frank said.

"Did Opal come, too?"

"Naw," Joe said. "She never wants to go anywhere 'cept run off in the woods and hide."

Frank wore his best seersucker pants, yellow polo

shirt, and someone had cut his hair. Leota Ritter clung to his arm. She was attractive enough, slim, with brown hair, blue eyes, and a neat blue dress, though I couldn't see any reason Frank had to be making eyes at her the way he was.

The Reeders were there. I went off with J.W. We inspected the pies and cakes. My mouth watered in anticipation.

J.W. pointed out Charley Watson and Cleburn Pounds, the two school teachers at Bohannon. Cleburn Pounds had written a song about his girl friend, titled, *Corrina, Corrina, Where You Been So Long*, which Bob Wills and his Texas Playboys had recorded.

When it got dark, the older people went into the house and sang religious songs. We kids played outside in the moonlight. The other boys scared me. They were rowdy, and some wanted to know why we kids weren't in school. All wanted to wrassle me, to establish the pecking order. I didn't want to. I didn't like fussing and fighting. Besides, Papa would whip me if he found out.

I thought the women would never cut the pies and cakes. About ten p.m. they finally did. I tried to sample each. This was a treat we didn't often get at home. I wrapped four pieces of cake in a napkin for Opal, Betty, Hazel, and Pete, and placed them in my hat.

I decided to go back home with the other boys instead of going on to Uncle Bryan's. We walked in a close group for protection. Frank and Leota and Jess Haynes and Pansy Reeder walked on ahead so they could spark. When we got to the Reeders', we waited while Frank walked Leota on home.

Loren worried about Peat Hacker's Nance. "Man, I wouldn't walk up there by myself at night."

"Aw," I scoffed, "there ain't nothin' to be scared of. Papa says there ain't no such thing as a ghost."

"There's panthers in the woods," Loren insisted. "Come up here from the Ki-mish all the time, huntin'."

This started us talking about panthers and foxes. By the time Frank got back, the moon had set. As we walked on home, the woods seemed like a different place. It wouldn't take much to believe in "haints" and "painters" on a night like this. I tried to dismiss the thought from my mind.

When we got to the lonesome pine, Frank began to sing: *"Oh, they cut down that old pine – "*

A loud snarl rudely interrupted his words. A shadowy form leaped from a low branch and landed in the road.

I dropped the cake and my hat. "Panther!"

Chapter 8

THE DOGS

The shadowy form crouched in the road and snarled. A chill crept down my spine. Frank slipped out his pocketknife and Joe and I each threw a rock. The animal leaped into the brush and crashed off through the canyon.

"What was it?" Joe spoke hoarsely.

My knees still shook. "Panther."

"Naw," Frank disagreed. "Too little and light-colored for that."

"Then what in the heck was it?" I demanded.

"Bobcat. Or maybe gist a big old housecat."

"Housecat your hindleg," I said imitating Papa. "Ain't no housecat sounds like that."

"Well, we'll see in the mornin'," Frank said. "We'll come back and look for tracks."

We started on. I had lost my cap and the cake.

Next morning, Papa returned with us. We found my hat. Ants crawled all over the cake. Papa studied several large paw prints in the road. He peered in the bushes.

"Bobcat," he said, verifying Frank's opinion. "About twenty-five pounds, eatin' one of Miz Reeder's guineas."

"How do you know?" I blurted.

He showed us how the paw prints did not sink into the

soft sand very deeply, the tawny fur caught on the brush, and the speckled feathers in the grass beneath the pine.

"Learn to read sign," he said. "It'll tell you a lot."

I felt relieved it wasn't a panther. A little bobcat wouldn't bother much. "You goin' to git him for killin' Miz Reeder's guinea?"

Papa shook his head. "Naw, the wild animals are havin' as hard a time as we are. It's their nature to make a livin' the best way they can, too."

It never ceased to amaze me how much Papa knew about the woods and animals.

Though we were eating some off the garden now, and Papa was making a little money, it was still a constant struggle to survive. We all needed clothes and were barefoot. I didn't mind for myself, but it bothered Frank and Opal. Opal ran to the woods, when anybody came.

The garden set on in abundance. Papa planted two rows of peanuts. March and I kept busy chasing the rabbits out of the garden. Once in awhile, I killed one, but Papa wouldn't let us eat it.

"They's poor and diseased this time of year," he said.

March's fur had grown slick. Her long lips hung in folds. Sometimes, I called her "Blabberlip" because, when she barked, she "blabbed" or "bawled." I thought a lot of her. She was pretty, a typical back and tan hound.

One day, while we were hoeing the corn, I heard March baying. She had something cornered across the clearing. Papa was out of sight. I ran to see what March had. It was a black beetle. She cuffed it about. I became absorbed in watching the beetle.

"What in Sam Hill are you a doin' up there?" Papa suddenly hollered at me.

I jumped, startled. "It's a bug," I spoke quickly. "March has treed a bug."

Papa came to look. "That's the way pups learn. First trailin' bugs, maybe terrapins, then chasin' squirrels."

I was anxious to hold his attention so he wouldn't get me for not working. "But that old bug was buried in the ground. How'd March know it was there?"

"She smelled him. Now you better git on back to work. We'll start trainin' that dog soon."

I returned to my hoeing, gratified Papa hadn't switched me and with my head full of new thoughts. We all craved meat. Soon, with March's help, maybe we would have plenty of squirrels.

A day or two later, when Papa came home from work, he had a second surprise. "I got us another dog. I think we'll need two of 'em for huntin'. Tag, in the mornin' you walk over to George Bishop's and git it."

Elation swept over me. I didn't mind the prospect of the seven-mile walk each way. Getting out of work and having two dogs would make up for that.

I got to the Bishops' about noon. Their family was a big one, all of them happy, friendly people. Mr. Bishop invited me to dinner. I was hoping he would. I was never too shy around others, talkative, and I liked to eat as well as Papa did.

As soon as I ate, I started back with the pup. Another hound, he looked about like March, except more tanish.

When I got home, Papa examined the dog. "He's got good marking's. He'll make a good squirrel dog."

In about two weeks, though, the dog began having fits. Papa said he had sore mouth and hook worms. Afraid he might infect March, he took the pup out in the woods and shot him. This left a hurt and empty place in me. I clung even closer to March.

A few days later, Papa came home with still another pup, a little black and tan pup that looked just like March.

"Where did you get him?" I asked, delighted.

"From Felix Bailey. He's a full brother to March. Out

of the same litter. Frank Bailey had given him to Felix, his brother. I traded Felix outa him."

"What'd you trade, Papa?" Joe asked.

"That old truck." Papa nodded towards the truck. It had sat idle since the day Papa had taken the gun to town, because he didn't have the money for gas. "Swapped for a little Ford runabout and the dog." Papa stroked the dog. "Felix called him 'Old Rattler' but I don't like that name. We'll call him Rex.'"

I patted my hands. "Here, Rex." I gathered the dog into my arms. He felt soft and smelled good like March.

"Now, don't you go spoilin' that dog like you done March," Papa scolded. "They's not house dogs."

"I won't," I said, knowing I would.

Right off, Rex proved more aggressive than March. If you scolded March, she would tuck her tail between her legs and sneak off. Rex wouldn't. He had a lot of spirit and would growl in defiance. I teased him, getting down on my knees and glaring at him. He showed his teeth, as if he were going to bite me. I mocked him and spit at him. He jumped and snapped at me. We were only playing so I wasn't afraid of him.

I loved that dog almost at once. We all did. We fed Rex and March table scraps. One day, when Papa was gone, the dogs began to howl and run in circles. I tried to catch Rex. He snapped at me.

Fear gushed through me. I ran to the tent. "Mama! Somethin's wrong with the dogs! They've got the runnin' fits like that pup!"

She hurried to see. "Quick! You kids get in the tent. If they bite you while havin' a fit, you'll have one, too!"

I didn't know whether this was true or not, but it terrified me to think March and Rex might have to be destroyed like the pup. I could hardly stand it until Papa got home from work.

"Have they got the hook worms and sore mouth, too?" I asked fearfully.

He watched the dogs a bit and asked us how they had acted all day. "Sounds more like pin worms to me." He opened the shoebox, where he kept his important papers, and took out a little, brown veterinary book. He looked up the remedy for worms. "Give 'em two or three spoonsful of turpentine," he read.

"Papa, we ain't got no turpentine," Joe reminded.

"Law! You kids! We got a whole woods full of it!"

Joe and I went with Papa to the spring and collected a double-handful of rosin, seeping from the large pines, where bore worms had been at work.

Papa melted the rosin in a pan. He molded the rosin in marble-sized chunks. He wrapped the chunks in a biscuit sopped in gravy and fed the biscuit to the dogs. In two or three days, March and Rex began to pass the worms and got well. I hugged the dogs in relief.

Papa observed the dogs each day as we worked. Rex and March treed bugs, then terrapins. When the dogs went to baying, we all dropped our hoes and ran to see what they had. The dogs trailed the terrapins and pawed at them.

One day, Papa said, "It's time we started trainin' these dogs in earnest."

The Peace family had left two mature cats behind. The cats had turned half-wild and lived off mice and birds. One of the cats had two half-grown kittens. Joe and I caught one of these kittens, then while Papa held the dogs, we took the kitten into the woods and chased it off. Papa turned the dogs loose. They smelled the cat's trail and took after him, bellering and yelping. They treed him a half-mile away and sat down at the foot of the tree, baying.

Papa petted Rex and March. "Good dog! Good dog!"

Sometimes, we'd pitch one of the old cats out of the crib and send the dogs after it.

After the dogs learned to trail the cats, Papa killed a squirrel and dragged it a half-mile through the woods.

When Joe and I turned the dogs loose, they trailed the squirrel until they found Papa.

Working with the dogs almost let us forget our other problems. Nevertheless, Papa remained in constant conflict with his men on the WPA. One day, somebody slipped a mountain boomer into the syrup pail, which he used as a lunch bucket. Harold and Sanford McNutt hid at the side of the road and threw rocks at Papa. This made me angry. I knew they had heard bad things about Papa from their dad, Buford McNutt.

Once, when I went to the mailbox, I found a letter from Bud and Eunice with two dollars in it, wadded up and thrown in the mud. This happened twice more. We suspected the McNutt boys. Papa had all of it he could tolerate.

His eyes squinched. "Now they's messin' with the U.S. mail. Soon as I git to town, I'm goin' to turn this matter over to the U.S. postal inspector."

Before Papa could do that, Frank came home. "Papa," Frank said, "ain't no use gittin' ever'body madder at us than they already are. Gist leave it to me. I'll git it stopped."

Papa didn't know how, but I knew Gloe McNutt, Harold and Sanford's sister, was a real nice girl and a good friend of Leota Ritter. That night at singing, Frank must have said something to Gloe, and she to her dad. We had no more trouble with the mail.

June sat on the clearing in full bloom. When we weren't hoeing, cutting wood, or cleaning up brush, we were helping Mama can vegetables. One day, Pete went to the corn patch with Mama. He came back, carefully holding his hands two feet apart. He held his hands up against a canning jar, measuring it.

He shook his head. "She c-can't do it."

"Do what?" I asked, wondering what his four-year-old mind had come up with this time.

"Mama c-cain't git that c-corn in them jars," he stuttered. "Them s-stalks, they's too b-big!"

I bent over laughing. "You dummy! Mama has to pull the ears off the stalks, then cut the corn off the cob!"

The weather grew hotter as June increased. Papa built Mama a brush arbor at the tent entrance. Mama and the girls moved the table, chairs, and bench out there. Somewhere, Papa obtained a small, legless, iron cookstove. He set this on flat sandrocks under the arbor, and Mama did her cooking and canning there, where it was cooler.

Joe and I moved our iron bedstead outside under a hickory. At night, we gazed at the stars, listened to the whipporwills, and felt the cool breeze touch our faces. I never wanted to go back to the city.

When Papa went to work, he left Joe in charge of the work on the clearing. At noon, we kids fussed over who got to sit in Papa's chair at the head of the table.

Mama went about her work patiently. For the most part, she seemed content though she never went anywhere. She had a sense of humor, but seldom exercised it when Papa was around. She was always threatening to tell Papa if we kids didn't behave.

"Mama," I asked once, "why don't you gist whip us yourself and git it over with?"

She grinned. "No use barkin' when you got your own dog."

I was more rambunctious than the other kids. Mama was forever warning me: "You better watch your *p*'s and *q*'s, young man. Your daddy'll skin your hide."

In my free time, I roamed the woods with the dogs, reveling in the life we led, though the work was hard. Occasionally, Lem Hatcher drove by the clearing, flinty-eyed. When I saw him in the woods, I remained hidden. I was careful not to roam over on his side of Boggy Creek.

Mr. Bishop told Papa that Lem Hatcher had castrated George Williams' bull. The animal had gotten into Hatcher's corn patch. Instead of shutting the bull up and telling Williams about it, Hatcher had driven the bull into his horselot and castrated him, ruining the bull's value. I kept my hand on March and Rex, when Hatcher was about. I didn't trust that sneaky look in his little green eyes.

Papa ignored Lem Hatcher the best he could and kept to his business. Papa believed the best way to get anything was to work for it. His favorite platitude was: *"Honest labor bears a lovely face."* It was work that produced the things "a-body" needed. So, Papa kept the wheels of industry on the clearing humming.

We kids were not driven to keep busy all the time like Papa. The girls, in particular, did not like field work. In those days, few girls worked outside the house. However, Papa was never one to stand on convention.

He continually scolded us for leaving a gate down, or not taking proper care of our tools. One day, he picked up the crosscut saw and snorted in exasperation. "I'd gist like to know what in the Sam Hill you young uns been a cuttin'. Don't take care of nothin'. Saw right slap-dab through a log into the rocks. If it ain't one John Brown thing, it's another. I know in my time I do git aggravated!"

He set about to sharpen the saw. "I'd do it Saturday," he grumbled, "but I got to walk over to the main road and try to catch a ride to town and sign up."

"Sign up for what?" Mama asked.

"I won't know 'til I git to town," Papa answered, "but they'll be somethin'. Always is. It's been this way ever since Roosevelt got in office. But maybe he can git us outa this Depression. Won't have to cut posts for peas. Won't have to use a saw someone else throwed away. May have a little sidemeat to eat, new overalls, and shoes to wear."

He took the saw and set a cane-bottomed chair by a red oak stump. He put on his dimestore bifocals and fumbled in a wooden Cloverbloom cheese box for his cob-handled Black Diamond file.

He cut a slot in the stump to hold the saw, teeth up. He called to Joe and me. "Come here. Now watch, they's an art to sawin'. A saw cuts on the push stroke. When you pull the saw back, raise it up gist a smidgeon, then shove. That's what does the cuttin', the push stroke. Your partner on the other end only guides. Then, when he pushes, you guide."

He sighted down the teeth of the saw, checking the "set" of the teeth. He explained how the vee-shaped teeth, the "carriers," carried the sawdust out, and how the sharp-pointed ones, the "cutters" did the cutting.

He filed the sawdust carriers first; then the cutters. He sent me to the tent for a meat rind with which to oil the saw. He polished the saw blade with a small sandstone. Then, he tried out the saw on the stump. He looked up with a grin.

"Cuts sharp as a north wind. Your old daddy knows his okra, when it comes to a saw," he said.

Papa applied this same confidence and resourcefulness to his job on the WPA. There, the men appreciated it less. Grumbling increased among the men to have him thrown off the job. Buford McNutt, in particular, did not like him. One day, in an altercation over some order, Buford threatened to whip Papa. That night, when Mama opened Papa's lunch bucket to wash it, she jerked her hand back and screamed. Out of the bucket crawled a tarantula.

Papa killed the tarantula with a stick of stovewood, his face grim. "I'm goin' to put a stop to this. Tarantulas ain't that poison, but, when people go to scarin' others with 'em, that's enough."

Chapter 9

LAID BY

Papa was a man who tried hard to get along with others. He tolerated a lot, but one thing he wouldn't take was anyone giving Mama a hard time, not even us kids.

The next morning, he walked over to Mr. Romine's. The two drove to Stuart and called Tom Anglin in Holdenville. Mr. Romine reported the trouble Papa was having as overseer on the road work. About 1:30 that afternoon, Sheriff Harve Ball, drove up to Papa and the men working on the road.

"Boys," Sheriff Ball said, "I don't know all the petty details about what goes on down here, but this is a federal job. The first one of you that hurts Mr. Speer – or his family – Tom Anglin and I will see you are sent to the penitentiary at Ft. Leavenworth. So let's drop this nonsense and all work together."

His words carried weight. Papa's trouble on the job simmered down. In two weeks though, the project ran out of money, and all the men were laid off.

Shortly after, Buford McNutt's barn burned. The rumor spread that we had done it, but we wondered if the fire was set by the same one who had fired our brush fence, creating further agitation to get us off the clearing.

With the loss of Papa's job, things on the clearing grew tighter. July came in hot and dry. The Oklahoma wind lifted the dust high into the sky. The plants in the garden wilted. We carried endless buckets of water from the spring to save the tomatoes. Neighbors hauled water from Pine Springs in a ceaseless caravan.

Papa scanned the sky, hoping to see a black cloud. He shook his head and profoundly noted, "In time of dry weather, all signs of rain fail."

His debts pressed him. Frank still worked at Romine's trying to pay for the cow and other things Papa kept getting over there. One day, when Frank was home, Papa and Frank started to town in the little runabout truck. The truck threw a rod and ran a piston through the engine block. Albert Reeder offered to take the truck in payment for the ten dollars Papa still owed him on the clearing. Papa gladly accepted the deal. Hardly anybody had any money those days. Most transactions were carried out by barter.

One day, Earl Lane came by the clearing, peddling a calf he had butchered. "I don't have much left," he apologized to Papa.

Papa peered into the wagon. "What'cha got?"

"A piece of brisket and a few soup bones. That brisket ain't much account. Comes from the neck."

Papa's eyes shone. He had been a butcher and knew the brisket was a delicacy. "What'll you take for it?"

"'Bout anything you got."

Papa traded him two buckets of tomatoes for the meat. That night, we sat down to a feast. Papa chuckled about getting the "best part of the beef." Next day, Mama canned some of the backbone and tail for soup.

The following week, Papa traded a guitar that Charley McClure had made to Albert Reeder for an old, sandy-colored, razorback sow.

We built a pen for the sow out of red oak poles. We walked down to the Reeders' after the sow. Papa swore she was "poorer than Job's turkey." He tied a small rope around her left hindleg so we could drive her home.

That proved no easy matter. The sow seemed bent on going every place, but where we wanted her. With Papa holding onto the rope and Joe and I pushing and pulling, we finally got her home. Papa split a hollow tree and made her a slop trough. He set us kids to pulling pigweed, ragweed, careless weeds and lamb's quarter to feed her. This took about an hour each day.

Even with the summer heat, we were never idle on the clearing. We worked from "can see to can't see," as Papa put it.

I flopped down wearily one day. "Mama, what does Papa do? Gist lie awake at night thinkin' up things for us kids to do?"

Her gray eyes lit with humor. "You better watch out, that old man'll skin your hide."

He probably would have if he had heard me. He didn't have much patience with laziness.

I grumbled to Joe about the continual work.

"What else you got to do?" he replied stoically.

"Well, I'd like to go fishin' or do somethin' else, once in awhile."

As often as I could, I went fishing on Saturday afternoons, walking down to Uncle Bryan's or going with Mr. Reeder down on Boggy.

Mr. Reeder was getting old and Mrs. Reeder liked for someone to go with him. But Albert preferred going to the singing on Saturdays, and neither J.W. nor Loren liked to go, because Mr. Reeder scared them all the time with ghost stories.

His stories didn't bother me much. Not unless he got to talking about people who had died and their spirit flying out the window with a devil on one shoulder and an angel on the other, fighting to see which one was going to get it. Besides, Mrs. Reeder always packed us a good supper.

Late one hot July day, I hustled down the sandy road to go fishing with Mr. Reeder. Mr. Reeder had old Babe hitched to the buggy with a quilt inside, some fried pies, along with some guinea eggs for supper, and his fish hooks in a bucket.

"You sorry-lookin' Pete," he greeted. "You better larn to move faster or a Yahoo'll ketch you." He grinned, his yellow handlebar mustache twitching above his six, yellow-stained, snaggled teeth.

J.W. fetched him a fresh-killed rabbit for bait.

"Come go with us," I urged.

"Naw, it's too far and snakey. I'm goin' over to Alley's and mess around."

A devilish twinkle glistened in Mr. Reeder's eyes. "He's feared Peat Hacker's Nance'll git him."

Mr. Reeder and I drove over to Rock Creek, where it runs into Boggy Creek. Mr. Reeder said the catfish like to lay in the deep holes there during the hot summer months. He crawled from the buggy, his scrawny figure stiffly erect, tied Babe to a tree, and fed her some corn.

"Taw-ig, you go cut us some poles."

"You betcha."

In a few minutes, I was back with a dozen slender willows. Mr. Reeder fixed a short line on the end of each and tied on hooks and sinkers. We baited each hook with a piece of rabbit. He set the poles along the bank. We built a fire. Mr. Reeder made some coffee and boiled the guinea eggs in it. We took a look at the fishing poles and came back and ate.

After supper, Mr. Reeder leaned back against a tree and smoked his pipe in contentment. I sat cross-legged on the quilt. Night had come. The firelight flickered amongst the leaves. A smoky lantern cast a yellow circle on the ground. An owl hooted somewhere and another answered.

I glanced up. "Listen to them owls."

Mr. Reeder's eyes glistened. "'Em ain't owls. 'Em is

Yahoos. They'll kirry off sorry-lookin' boys like you that'll lay aroun' and let their old daddy do all the work."

"There ain't no such thing as Yahoos."

He cackled. "You'll find out someday." His gaze roamed the creek bank. "Take this yhar creek now, the Spaniards was yhar."

I settled myself comfortably, knowing a story was coming.

Mr. Reeder took a long puff on his pipe. "When I furst came yhar into this part of the country, after the Civil War, the North had a lot of gold they was takin' west along the Santa Fe Trail to pay the soldiers who'd been fightin' out this way. Somehow, the Yankee paymaster wandered off the trail. The Spaniards come 'crost him, cut his throat, and stole that gold and buried it. They figgered on comin' back after it someday, but nivver did. History books say it's lost forever, but," he leaned forward a little, "I know whar that gold is."

My skin prickled. "Where?"

His voice lowered. "In a canyon west of the house."

"How do you know?"

"Wal, one day, when I was out huntin' in the woods, it got to rainin' and lightin'. I hunkered back agin a rock to git outa the wet. To pass the time, I picked up a stick and started whittlin'. My knife slipped. When it did, the end of it hit that rock. That rock sounded holler. I examined it real close. I found a door in thar with moss coverin' it. The door had some Spanish signs on it. I got that door open and looked inside. Thar was a little room dug 'neath the rock. I couldn't see much, so I jumped into the hole. Thar in that cave was stacked gold bullion, bars and bars of it. Thar must of been ten jackass loads of it in thar."

My eyes widened. "Wow! What'd you do?"

"Wal, when the rain stopped, I found I couldn't get outa the cave. 'Twas deeper than I thought. I could barely touch the top of the openin' by runnin' and jumpin'. Finally, I caught one finger up over the edge and hung thar four or five minutes, restin'. Then, I got my whole hand up over the edge and begin pullin' myself up out of thar. My toes kept slippin' agin' the slick side. But, I kept pushin' and squirmin'. I caught hold of a little old root at the edge of the openin', and pulled myself outa thar. I put that door back in place so's nobody else could find that gold."

"Did you ever go back and git it?" I asked eagerly.

"Wal, it was this a way." Mr. Reeder lifted his black hat and scratched his balding head. "I was so excited and tard time I got outa thar I nivver could 'member after that exactly which canyon it was in. I looked an looked. But nothin' was the same. I figgered the ghosts of them Spaniards come back and changed how it looked around thar so I couldn't find it." The light played on his weathered face in an eerie manner.

I swallowed. "Aw, there ain't no ghosts." I could never quite tell about Mr. Reeder, whether he really believed all these stories himself. I didn't tell him I knew the Spaniards were gone long before the Civil War.

He rambled on, telling me about fishing with a hay hook and a rope and of baiting his hook with a whole chicken. Then, he told about the time when he was a boy in Kentucky and twenty wolves chased his team of mules and wagon. Each time the wolves got close, he shot one and the others gobbled it up and took up pursuit again. Finally, there was only one wolf left. He kept getting closer and closer. About that time, the mules hit a stump, knocked a wheel off the wagon, and run off.

"Weren't you scared?" I asked.

"Naw," he replied, straight-faced. "They wasn't but one wolf left and he was full by then."

Occasionally, Mr. Reeder and I checked our fishing

poles. About midnight, we had another snack, built up the fire to chase off the mosquitoes, and laid down on the quilt. Mr. Reeder talked on, telling me about the time he was a Texas Ranger and more gold hunting stories. I could barely stay awake. Finally, Mr. Reeder dropped off to sleep and snored gently through his mustache. The stillness settled over the creek. There was no moon. I could hear the gentle slap of water, frogs croaking, and crickets chirping.

At daylight, we ran our lines again. We had six catfish. Some weren't too big.

"You wanta throw these little uns back?" I asked.

"Naw," Mr. Reeder said. "If they're big enough to bite, I figger they're big enough to eat."

He took them all home to clean. I didn't want any. Our family didn't care much for catfish.

When we got back, I thanked Mr. Reeder for the fishing trip and said I best be getting on home.

"What all ya been plantin' over thar lately?" he asked.

"Well, it seems to me like we been plantin' more whipporwill peas than anything else," I complained. "We got peas in the bean rows, peas in the corn rows, peas everywhere."

"Wal, this winter you sorry-lookin' boys won't do nothin' but lay aroun' and fart." Mr. Reeder's eyes twinkled with his snaggle-toothed grin.

I walked back to the clearing, tired but content. I told Mama what Mr. Reeder said about the whipporwill peas, and she laughed. Papa sat under a tree reading his Bible.

I flopped down beside him. "Papa, with all them gold stories of Mr. Reeder's, you think he ever really found any?"

Papa squinched up his eyes and snorted. "Law! The only gold that old man ever found was at the end of a hoe handle."

July continued to bear down on the clearing, hot,

windy, and dry. The corn shriveled and the thin leaves rustled in the wind. Dry weather clouds floated across the sky. Turkey buzzards hung in the updrafts, waiting for the inevitable. March and Rex dug cool hollows in the shade.

Most of the crops were "laid by" the middle of the month. Papa gazed in despair at the field corn, wilting in the blazing sun.

"I don't think the corn is goin' to make it. The only way we're goin' to be able to save any of it is to git out there and pull that fodder, or we won't have anything for that cow this winter."

Joe, Opal, Papa, and I began early the next morning, when the dew was still on so the leaves would not be so brittle. We stripped the leaves off the corn stalks and gathered the leaves in bundles and tied them with another leaf. We shuffled back and forth, carrying the bundles to the smaller log crib. It was a hot, dirty, itchy job.

We husked the ears and laid the corn in the sun to dry. Later, we would rub the immature kernels from the cobs. Papa would have the corn ground into cornmeal, paying the miller with a portion of the meal.

We picked blackberries along the fence rows. The tomatoes had come on in abundance. We fed the excess to the sow. About a month after we brought her home, she had nine little pigs. She smashed two and another died.

Bohannon school took up for a summer session in mid-July. It was to continue for six weeks, then let out until the first of November. This way families could benefit from the children's labor, when it came time to gather the crops.

All spring and summer, I wondered if we would get to go to school when it opened. I hoped so for I liked to read and learn. However, we didn't get to go, as none of us had the clothing. Besides, Papa needed us to work.

Rumors spread that Papa was violating the law by not sending us to school. George Gould, whose father was on the schoolboard, told me one day at Sunday School that the schoolboard was going to send the truant officer after us and send Papa to the penitentiary. This scared me. The next weekend, when I was walking down to Uncle Bryan's, Charley Watson, the school teacher, stopped me at the foot of Hickerson Hill and asked when we were going to enroll. I told him as soon as we could. I told Papa about this later.

"Well, I know I'm violatin' the law," he said, "but I need you here now. I figger it's more important to feed you than educate you right now."

August came without any letup in the heat. We did the bulk of our work in the early morning or evening. The only cool place here was down by the spring.

Bugs and scorpions crawled inside the tent seeking shelter. One day, a garter snake got into a drawer. Opal touched the snake, screamed, and burst into hysterical tears. "I hate this place! I wish I was back in Tulsa!"

The cane stood limp in the heat. The gooseneck maize looked as if it were dying, too.

Papa's barrel-chest heaved. "We better save all we can."

Joe, Papa, Opal, and I cut the maize heads, let them dry a day or two and stacked them in the crib. We tied the stalks into bundles and stood them in shocks like Indian tepees to dry out for winter hay for the cow.

Frank still worked at Romine's. He came home on Saturday evenings and went back on Monday mornings. Each time he thought he about had that cow paid for, Papa would go back and get something else to eat.

Frank's bondage weighed heavily upon him. Jess Haynes and Pansy Reeder were talking about getting married. Frank had been courting Leota Ritter rather seriously ever since we moved onto the clearing. Nineteen years old, he wanted to get married, too. He objected to the way Papa kept him obligated to Mr. Romine without even asking him about it.

The two Romine girls teased Frank constantly about Leota. One day, Mr. Romine gave Frank a letter from Leota, which he said had come there and been opened by mistake. Frank wondered by whom? In addition, Frank felt self-conscious in his ragged clothes and out of place in the Romines' home.

One Saturday, when Frank came home, he had taken about all he could stand. "I've had enough," he told Papa. "I ain't goin' back over there to work."

Papa and Mama stared at him. Fear darkened Mama's eyes. Without Frank's help, none of us knew what we would do. Mama had been counting desperately on having that cow soon.

Chapter 10

THE BEE TREE

We sat silent for a long moment, absorbing Frank's startling announcement. The sun had set. A fly landed on the table. Mama absently brushed the fly away with the back of her hand.

I had always been partial to Frank. He would not boss us kids around or tell on us. He would let me go with him, when he went somewhere. He had a feeling for all the family. He showed me how to do things and played with Pete. He drew pictures for the other kids and helped Mama around the tent. He seldom fussed or grumbled about anything. Once in awhile, he might get angry with us kids, but he did not flare up like Perry did. Frank was a good worker. Occasionally, he and Papa would disagree over how to do something, but Frank always gave in.

This time was different, however. I could see Frank was in no mood to bend to anyone's will.

Evidently, Papa could see it, too. "What you figgerin' on doin'? You gotta have a job. Gotta eat."

Frank shoved back his chair. "I know that. You guys can sit here and starve if you want to, but I'm goin' to pack my duds and go to Tulsa. Goin' to git me a job with a paycheck ever' week. Goin' to eat Post Toasties, light bread, and Pork and Beans; live a little for a change."

"How you goin' to do all that? Ain't no jobs in Tulsa. Ain't no jobs anywhere," Papa said.

"Cousin 'Little Charlie' is makin' fifty cents an hour in Tulsa, layin' steel."

"Ain't no man worth fifty cents an hour."

"That's what he's gittin'. Me, I'm goin' up to Tulsa, try to git on. If I can't find somethin' up there, I'll come back and try to find a job pickin' cotton. Right now, I'm tired of feelin' like somebody's slave, of never gittin' nowhere, of havin' nothing' to look forward to but tryin' to farm with some old rusty tools, and eatin' 'soaky bread' or cornbread for breakfast."

Frank's black eyes burned with his words. I knew how he felt. We had plenty of vegetables and once in awhile a squirrel, but for breakfast, we never had anything but soaky bread or cornbread.

You made soaky bread by putting a biscuit in a cup and pouring a little sweetner and coffee over it. When Mama didn't have any flour for biscuits we ate cornbread for breakfast. People considered this low on the social scale. When you had biscuits, that meant you had a little money with which to buy flour. Cornmeal you made yourself. I disliked eating soaky bread for breakfast as much as anybody. Most often, we ate it without any sweetner, or worse yet, we ate cornbread.

Papa rubbed his aching feet. "Well, Frank, I reckon you're old enough to make up your own mind about things, what you wanta do. But they's nowhere to go. The whole country's hit by this Depression. You'd be better off to stay in the woods and with the land."

Frank's mouth tightened. "I don't see how you figger."

"If a man's a good enough woodsman, he can always find somethin' to eat."

"Yeah," Frank agreed with a humorless laugh. "Well, I'd like to see you find somethin' besides soaky bread and cornbread for breakfast."

Papa's eyes lit. "A'right, I will." He left the table.

Mama cleared the dishes. Frank stared in dejection at his bare feet and sucked at his tongue through his teeth, the way he always did when thinking.

The next morning, Frank still looked upset. He and Joe left for Sunday School at Bohannon church. The younger kids seldom went because it was so far to walk. Opal wouldn't go because of her lack of clothes. I didn't go this morning because I had a stone bruise and my old broken down shoes hurt my feet.

I teased Pete a bit, then romped with Rex and March. It was a clear, warm morning. Papa stood at the edge of the clearing, looking thoughtful. I wondered how he was going to meet Frank's challenge about finding something else for breakfast. Privately, I thought he should have kept quiet.

Papa turned. "Tag, git the axe and come along. I want to show you how to do somethin'."

I went at once, sensing something new in the offing. "Where we goin'?"

"To find a bee tree."

"A bee tree? Papa, you know Alley Reeder's found every bee tree within five miles of here."

"He ain't found one of 'em. Alley Reeder ain't the only one that knows his way around in the woods."

I grabbed the axe and followed him west from the clearing, past the pigpen, and toward Pine Spring. Rex and March followed, noses to the ground, tails "ringing."

When we reached the spring, Papa sat down on a rock. He gazed at the water, then the trees, where the sunlight filtered through the leaves. I couldn't figure out what Papa was doing. He just sat a long time looking. I thought he'd blown his top.

Finally, Papa pointed at the spring. "See them bees?"

There were dozens of them, crawling around at the edge of the water, drinking, then darting off among the timber.

"Yeah."

"Now look at 'em close. Them bees are not goin' very far from here."

"How do you know that?"

"Well, if a bee is goin' a long ways off, he'll go straight up, about a hundred feet or so in the air, then dart off. If he's goin' somewhere close, within a quarter-mile say, he'll gist angle straight for the tree he's in." He pointed southwest in the direction the bees were going. He stood. "Come on, let's go this way."

We climbed the ridge on the south side of the spring. Papa paused, studying the tree tops. "I don't see anything here. Come on."

We walked down the ridge about a half-mile into Mossy Hollow. A little branch ran in the bottom. Papa sat down and studied the bees crawling along the edge of the water. He observed their line of flight, when they took off.

He rose. "They's headin' back northeast. That bee tree is 'bout half-way between here and Pine Spring. Come on, we'll find it."

I followed him back up the ridge, thinking, 'Well, old man, of all the trees in the forest, how you going to find that particular one the bees are in?'

Papa walked ahead of me through the woods. He wore the top of his B.V.D.s and a pair of yellow, stripped suspenders. He never went bare-shouldered, because he sunburned easily. Squirrels chattered and bluejays scolded us. Occasionally, Papa gazed up through the trees. I wondered what he was doing and shook my head in amusement. I was hot and thirsty and didn't have any faith in what he was doing. March and Rex had headed back to the clearing.

Papa wandered along looking up. After a time, he laid down on the ground beneath a big post oak and folded his hands over his chest. I stared at him in shock. I thought, 'Boy, howdy, I'd better go home and git help. He is sick!'

Papa gazed into the treetop. Soon he said, "This is it. The bees are in this tree."

I looked up. I didn't see anything. "How do you know?"

"Come here and look."

I laid down beside him. Papa pointed. "Look real close, up through that openin' between the leaves and into the sky."

I stared hard at the patch of blue. Suddenly, I could see the black dots criss-crossing.

"Now," Papa directed, "take your eye and go up this tree until you come to a knothole."

I saw it, about thirty-five feet above the ground. The bees were flying in and out the knothole. "Yeah, there they are! How in the world did you know that?"

Papa got up, pleased with himself. "Well, the timber on this ridge is scrubby. I knew the bees were between this waterhole and the other one. That give me a straight line between 'em. I looked. They's not over four or five trees in this scrub timber big enough for a bee tree. So, all I had to do – when you was follerin' back there, gigglin' and actin' a fool – was see where the bees was."

I ducked my head in shame. My respect for Papa came back immediately. "Well, what'll we do?"

"We'll mark the tree with the axe and go back to the tent. After dinner, them other boys'll be home. We'll come back and cut this tree down and git that honey."

"Today? This is Sunday." Papa never worked on Sunday.

"I know that," he said. "I know what the Bible says 'bout restin' on the Sabbath. It also says God made the Sabbath for man; not man for the Sabbath. This is somethin' I have to do. I think the Lord'll understand.

We blazed the tree and headed home, Papa walking fast now. "Here in mid-summer is the only time to rob the bees," he spoke over his shoulder. "Thata way, they'll have time to make more honey 'fore winter, and won't starve out."

Papa was always careful of the wild animals this way. He would never let us kill a squirrel or anything at the waterhole either. That was taking unfair advantage.

When we reached the tent, Joe was there. Frank had gone home with Leota Ritter for dinner. They planned to go back to the church-house to practice singing.

"That's a'right," Papa said.

He told the others about the bee tree. He asked Mama for an old curtain she had saved from our house in Tulsa. Joe and I got some buckets, a washtub, and the saw. Papa tied some rags on the end of a stick and soaked the rags in coal-oil. After we ate, Mama helped Papa tie the curtain over his hat and face. He put on his coat and buttoned it up, and slipped on a pair of gloves. "Let's go. Betty, you and Hazel keep them dogs here this time."

We went back to the bee tree. Joe and I sawed it down. It fell with a thunderous crash.

"We'll cut it up later for firewood," Papa said.

The bees buzzed angrily around the knothole. Papa lit the torch and smoked the bees to drug them. Joe chopped a notch in the tree trunk below the knothole and chopped it out. Golden honey oozed within. I grabbed a handful, tasted it, and let the pleasing sweetness run down my throat.

Papa watched me with a grin. "Yeah, I told you it was in there."

We filled three buckets and the tub. Mama clapped her hands, when she saw the honey. She and Opal melted the honey out of the combs and strained the liquid gold into clean jars. That evening, Mama baked a big pan of fluffy biscuits. We were just sitting down to what for us was a real feast, when Frank came in. He stared in wide-eyed amazement at the honey.

"Care to join us?" Papa invited with a toothless grin.

"We couldn't wait 'til breakfast."

Frank looked dumbfounded. "Where did you git all that?"

Papa looked smug. "I told you if a man is a good enough woodsman, he can always find somethin' to eat."

Frank sank down on the bench. "Well, maybe if a guy knew what you do, maybe he could live off the land and maybe he could make it. I been thinkin' all day, they's not much use of me goin' back up to Tulsa to look for work. I couldn't find any, when we lived up there. I probably wouldn't even have any soaky bread."

Papa's grin broadened.

Mama laid a comforting hand on Frank's shoulder. "Life ain't never easy, son." She handed him a plate.

"But," Frank added in warning, "Papa, you gotta quit goin' over to Mr. Romine's and gittin' stuff all the time."

Papa reached for the honey. "I'll try not to. You 'bout got that cow worked out. She's yourn. Someday, when you get married, I'll let you have her. Now the Lord has provided. Let's eat."

We all dived in, more than willing.

The next morning, before daylight, Frank walked back to Mr. Romine's as usual. The following weekend, when he came home, he led the cow.

"Mr. Romine said I don't have her quite worked out yet," he told Papa, "but he said I might as well bring her on over here. I guess he knows," he added ruefully, "that way I'll have to stay."

We named the cow Roady. She was a sleek Holstein with bulging sides. Three days later, she birthed a fat, spotted bull. Papa let the calf suckle for five days, then put him in a pen and taught him to drink from a bucket.

Mama milked the cow. Roady gave a bucket of milk each morning and evening. Mama skimmed the cream off the milk and stored it in half-gallon fruit jars in the spring. She made butter and cottage cheese. We had all the milk we wanted to drink.

One day, the NcNutt boys spilled the cream in the spring. Papa jumped Buford about it. Buford said he didn't know anything about it. Papa couldn't prove it, so like the rabbit, he had to let it go. However, messing with the spring, that hurt everybody.

Mr. Reeder gave Papa an old cowbell with a missing clapper. Papa tied a rusty nut inside with bailing wire. He fastened the bell around Roady's neck and turned her loose in the woods to forage. In the evenings, Rex and I listened for the bell and brought Roady home for milking.

Papa traded two of the pigs for a half-dozen laying hens and a rooster. With all our animals, the clearing was beginning to look and sound like a real farm.

Early in August, Papa heard the WPA was building a dirt dam close to Stuart. He walked over there and the overseer hired him for three days a week at two dollars a day. Each morning, Papa left for work long before daylight, walked nine miles, and returned late at night.

During his absence, Joe kept a close watch on the crops. One night, at the supper table, Joe said, "Papa, if we had us a mule or something to plow with, we could clear up some more new ground. Then, next spring, we could plant a lot more corn and fatten still more pigs. Maybe we could plant some cotton for a cash crop."

Papa leaned back in his chair. "Yeah, I've been thinkin' about that. I don't know any way in the world I could git a mule. Not unless I could git him on credit. Think I'll ask around at work, see if anybody knows of a mule for sale."

I liked the idea. A mule would save us a lot of work.

Opal had other thoughts. "Papa, how you goin' to pay for a mule? You want to buy everything on credit. Someday, you're going to have to pay that mule off, if you're lucky enough to find one." Opal, like Perry, wasn't afraid to speak up against Papa, something even Mama seldom did.

Papa tried to keep his voice even. "We'll work him out. This fall you kids can pick cotton around. We'll git him paid for. Sooner or later, we got to have one anyway, so I'll look around and see if I can buy one."

Opal looked stricken. "But you promised we could pick cotton to buy us some new clothes this fall. We're practically naked and everyone's barefooted!"

Papa's voice became testy. "I know that, girl. Don't tell me. I've thought about it. We'll manage somehow. Wait and see." His tone plainly warned her she had said enough.

Opal retired from the table, sullen and hurt.

Next day, when Papa returned from work, he looked pleased. "Well, I've got us a mule located. Em Hale, on the other side of Rock Creek, said he had a little red mule. I can buy him on credit and pay for him this fall."

Joe grinned. "When can we go after him?"

"Well, tomorrow's Saturday. You and me'll take a rope and go after him. I'll see 'bout gittin' some harness somewhere."

"Mr. Reeder said he had an old Georgia stock that you might could fix up," I said.

"I think Alley Reeder's got a couple of old plow points he can give us," Joe added.

Papa nodded. "I can fix 'em. I'll put Joe up there to plowin'. It'll save you kids a lot of diggin'."

Opal didn't look too happy, but the thought of getting a mule tickled me. Anything that would save us some work would be a blessing. Briefly, it crossed my mind, who owned this land? What would happen to all our hard work if someone claimed the land? I dismissed the thought. Hadn't nobody worried about the land on this ridge for fifty years. So why should they do so now?

Papa had got some sweet potato slips from Mr. Romine. Next morning, before Papa and Joe left to get the mule, Papa showed Opal, Betty, Hazel, and me how to set these out. It was late in the year, and Papa wasn't sure the sweet potatoes would make before frost. He hoed up several hills in a row and planted a sweet potato slip in one hill.

He paused in his work. "Now, see there. If I had a mule, I could gist throw them rows up there and have them slips all set in an hour."

Finishing, he dusted the knees of his worn overalls, and he and Joe set off at Papa's usual fast clip.

All morning, I could hardly wait for them to get back. About two o'clock I saw them coming. They didn't have a mule. The girls and I dropped our hoes and ran to the tent to meet them.

Papa told Mama, "Em Hale backed out on the deal."

I sank into a chair, disappointed. "Why?"

"Well, I'm not shore." Papa sat down and took off his shoes. "Em Hale said he'd been talkin' to some people. They told him times were goin' to be purty hard this fall. He didn't know if anybody could pay for that mule. He thought he better not let him go."

"Sounds funny to me," I grumbled, "changin' his mind all at onct."

Papa grunted in agreement. "There ain't much I can do about it. You kids best git on back to your work."

I dragged back to the field. I'd sure counted on that mule helping us.

That evening, about sundown, Frank walked in for the weekend. He brought some news for Papa: "Mr. Romine heard about your mule deal with Em Hale."

Papa looked only mildly surprised as news traveled fast in our small community.

"He found out why Em Hale backed out on you," Frank went on.

Papa stiffened. "Why?"

"Someone told him not to let you have that mule."

"Who?"

"Lem Hatcher."

Chapter 11

WE GET A MULE

Frank's words dropped among us like an exploding cartridge.

Papa's eyes flashed. "Let's hear it."

"Well," Frank began, "some way Lem Hatcher found out about you buyin' that mule. He told Em Hale he'd better be careful what he let you have on credit. He said your credit wasn't any good, and if the people who owned this land ever found out about you squattin' on it, they'd run you off."

"That dirty son-of-a-bitch!" Papa snapped.

Betty gasped. Papa seldom talked this way.

Papa glanced at her. "Now, that ain't cussin', you kids. That ain't takin' the Lord's name in vain."

Privately, I thought it didn't matter. That's what Lem Hatcher was, always sneaking around, asking us kids what we were doing, when Papa wasn't there, acting neighborly, but being nosey. We had left him alone, but he hadn't left us alone.

Papa's eyes squinched and his nose flared. "Dad-blamed that consarned man! I know in my time I do git aggravated. You do your best to git along with others, and that's the way they do in return."

Frank nodded. "Lem Hatcher is sure bent on gittin' you outa here. Mr. Romine told Em Hale to let you have that mule, that if you didn't pay for it, he would. Hale wouldn't do it. Hale's got them cattle down there by Hatcher. I guess he's afraid Hatcher'll do somethin' to them."

"Loren says them Hale boys probably git a little whiskey from Hatcher," Joe added.

Papa sat silent a moment. I could tell from his expression that his soul was fighting the will of God against the nature of man. The will of God won. Papa sighed. "Well, that's a'right. Maybe that wasn't the mule for me anyway. I'il git one some way. You wait."

I relaxed, knowing if Papa had made up his mind, not even Lem Hatcher could stop him.

The next day, Sunday, Uncle Bryan and Aunt Eula pulled into the clearing. Uncle Bryan drove Dick O'Daniel's team of black horses and his wagon, which was made out of the chassis of a Model-T Ford. Papa told Uncle Bryan about the mule deal.

Uncle Bryan shifted his billed cap to the back of his head. "Wal, Hen-a-ree, it 'pears to me lak ya need a mule yar, a'right. You could take in a leetle more of dat land up der for plowin', lak Joe sez. You know," he scratched his head, "I gist thought. I was workin' over thar at the blacksmith shop at old man O'Daniels' and I heered that Arthur Goodman had an old mule he needed to git shed of."

Papa leaned forward with interest. "Where does this bird, Goodman, live?"

"Wal, he lives directly east of yhar, 'bout four mile, if ye go through the woods, on the county line. Hen-a-ree, ye go see him. He lives up dere 'bout a mile north of old man George Gould. Mr. Gould can tell ye 'bout dat mule."

Papa leaned back, thinking on this. After dinner, when Uncle Bryan and Aunt Eula got ready to leave, Papa walked out with them. "I'll tell you what, Bryan. I'm goin' to ride over there a ways with you, then cut through the woods, and talk to this Goodman. See what he'll take for that mule."

"A'right," Uncle Bryan agreed.

Papa didn't get back until after sundown. We were waiting supper for him, some cornbread and sweetmilk. Papa sank into a cane-bottomed chair, bone-tired. "Well, I think we've got us a mule."

Joe grinned and tried to hide his teeth with his tongue. "Shore 'nuff?"

Papa nodded. "I could see him down in the pasture. They couldn't catch him. He's kinda skittish. Been in the pasture all spring."

"What does he look like?" I asked eagerly.

"He's a great big old thing, kinda poor. He can eat grass now, then this fall, we'll give him a little corn to fatten him up."

Joe settled back, satisfied. We both liked horses. When we lived in Tulsa, we went to the cowboy movies every Saturday. Our favorite stars were Tom Mix, Ken Maynard, Bob Steele, and Buck Jones. Joe and I dreamed of the day we could have a horse and saddle of our own, but a mule would do for now.

"Joe," Papa said, "early in the mornin', I want you and Tag to go down to Mr. Goodman's. Gist tell him who you are and that you've come after the mule. He said he'd feed him tonight and have him ready, when you got there."

Joe and I nodded and grinned at each other.

Opal's cheeks looked flushed. "Papa, you gittin' that mule on credit?"

Papa's eyes flashed in annoyance at her impertinent question. "I don't rightly see that's your business, but, yes, I am. Mr. Goodman said we could pick cotton for him this fall to help pay for him."

"How much does he cost?" she asked.

"Forty dollars. Now, that's enough of your pryin' into my business."

Opal stomped away. Sometimes, I wondered about her, the way she had been talking up to Papa lately. Buying a mule on credit didn't bother me. Nor did picking cotton. Anything would be better than working that new ground with a hoe.

Early next morning, I slipped on my ragged overalls and got my cap. Papa had gone to work. Joe found a long rope in the crib. We set out down the sandy road. March and Rex tried to follow. I sent them back. Rex whined, then trotted back to his favorite spot by the tent.

Joe and I reached the main road, cut through a field, and turned east past P.R. Davis'. We met Margaret and Marion Davis, riding their pony to school. They stared at us in curiosity, as we passed.

I cocked my cap. "Reckon they think we're a couple of movie stars?"

Joe grinned. "I 'magine."

It was five miles to Mr. Goodman's by the road. We got there about nine o'clock. Mr. Goodman was a tall, raw-boned man of about sixty. He had the mule penned up in the horselot.

"His name's Mike," Mr. Goodman informed us. "I had a team of mules. One of them drowned last spring, when the creek flooded. I'm needing another team. I can't match this mule. He's purty big."

That was for sure. Mike stood taller than I, thin, humped-back, brownish-black, with a white nose and a white star on his forehead.

I was real tickled. I walked up and petted the mule.

"Now, you'd better be careful," Mr. Goodman warned. "He's been in the pasture all spring and may be kinda wild."

I jerked my hand back, but Mike didn't do anything. I petted him and talked to him. Joe slipped the rope around the mule's neck, and we started home. Mike led easily. Joe and I felt as proud as if we led a parade.

After a mile, we stopped at a branch to let the mule drink. Joe gazed at the mule as if still unable to believe it. "A mule. We got us a shore 'nuff mule. Tag, I've a good notion to ride him."

I glanced at him, startled. "Joe, you gone plumb crazy? He'll throw you off. Man, that big old mule, he'll kill you. There ain't many mules been broke to ride like a horse. I wouldn't git on him."

"Aw, he won't do nothin'." Joe circled the mule. "I'm goin' to try it."

"Joe you better wait 'til we git a little closer home or somethin'," I fussed at him. "Then if you git hurt, I can git you on home."

Joe hesitated. "Aw, I don't want to walk that far. I'll tell you what let's do. Let's take a half-hitch around his nose with that rope. Then you snub him up real tight, where he can't git his nose down to buck, and I'll ride him."

I began to wonder if the mule might let us ride him.

"Lead him up to this stump," Joe urged, "and I'll see if he'll let me ride."

I stepped back. "No, you better not git on him. If he was to throw you or somethin' and Papa found out, he'd whip us both."

"Aw, bull. You hold his nose and I'll git on."

Reluctantly, I helped Joe tie a half-hitch around the mule's nose and led the mule to a stump.

Joe climbed upon the stump and prepared to mount. "Now you hold him good, you hear?"

I took a firm grip on the rope and braced my feet, expecting trouble. Joe settled his cap firmly then leaned against the mule, sort of hugging him. He laid his weight across the mule's back. Mike humped, flicked his tail, snorted, and backed his ears.

I paniced. "Joe, he's wild! See there! You better watch him!"

"Aw, he's a'right." Joe laid his weight across the mule

again. Mike didn't do much this time. Encouraged, Joe eased onto Mike's bony back, feet dangling on one side and head and arms on the other. "Lead him up the road a way."

Cautiously, I obeyed. Mike backed his ears and acted like he wanted to trot. I held him back. We approached an embankment.

Joe looked at it. "Stop. I'm goin' to git astraddle of him. He ain't goin' to do nothin'." He slid off the mule.

By this time, I could see Joe was right. I led Mike to the embankment. Joe climbed astride the mule.

Joe grinned and waved in triumph. "Tom Mix and Tony!"

I eyed him with envy. I led the mule about a quarter of a mile. It looked as if a shower might come up. We still had three miles to go. Mike seemed peaceable enough and Joe was enjoying himself.

Finally, I could stand it no longer. "Okay, let me ride him."

"A'right, I'll make a bridle," Joe said. "You can ride him that way."

"No," I balked. "I'm 'fraid. I'd druther you lead him."

"No, you're goin' to have to ride him by yourself."

I stood on one foot then the other. Thunder rumbled. "I'll tell you what," I decided. "Let's make a bridle and both of us ride him." I felt safer if something was to happen and Joe was responsible.

"A'right," Joe said.

Quickly, I fashioned the rope into a make-shift bridle around the mule's head and handed the ends to Joe. He gave me a hand up behind him. I settled down gingerly onto Mike's bony hips. Joe clucked to the mule. Mike moved forward without objecting to the added weight. It began to rain.

"Come on, mule, giddyap!" Joe touched his heels to Mike's flanks to hurry him along.

That proved the wrong thing to do. The next instant, Mike jerked up his head, and lit out down the road.

Joe see-sawed on the reins. "Whoa! Whoa!"

I clutched Joe's waist, trying to stay on.

"You dad-gummed mule!" Joe cried. "Whoa!"

The more he hollered, the faster Mike ran. We bounced around. The mule skidded on a slick spot. I slid to one side. Joe pulled me back on.

After about a mile, Mike began to slow, breathing heavily. Joe tightened the reins. "Hang on, I'm goin' to break him of that!"

He snapped a switch from a tree limb trailing overhead. He whipped the mule, making him run until his steps faltered. After that, the mule walked sedately on to the Reeders'. We got there just as the shower let up.

Joe glanced at the house. "Let's stop here and dry out a little. Looks like it might still be rainin' over home. Can't do much there until it stops."

"Sure." I knew Joe wanted to show off the mule.

Loren, J.W., Albert, and Mr. Reeder sat on the front porch, when we rode up. The collie and feist barked.

Mr. Reeder cackled. "Aw, ya sorry-lookin' Petes, what ya got thar?"

Joe and I slid stiffly to the ground.

"We bought a mule," Joe said.

"Wal, he looks like a purty good un, ya good for nothin' boys quit tryin' to ride him, and runnin' him all over creation."

Joe looked sheepish. "Yeah, we know, Mr. Reeder. It was rainin' and we wanted to get home as fast as we could."

"A little rain won't hurt ya. Ya ain't sugar. Ya won't melt."

The others came to the gate to look over the mule. "Where'd you get him?" Albert wanted to know.

"From Mr. Goodman," I said.

Loren squinted. "How old you reckon he is?"

Joe laughed. "Oh, 'bout fifty, I 'magine." Joe was funny that way. He didn't believe in telling others something he considered none of their business.

J.W. eyed the mule in admiration. "He's big enough."

"Well, he's a little on the thin side," Joe admitted, "but we'll fatten him up."

"At least we got somethin' to plow with now," I boasted, "if we can gist git us some harness."

Mr. Reeder leaned on his cane. "Goin' to be hard to fit. I might hev an old bridle out thar that'll go around him and a pair of hames your daddy could fix up. That is, if you two ornery boys ain't too lazy to git out thar and hunt for 'em."

"I'll go," I said at once.

Joe, Loren, and J.W. went with me. We found the bridle and hames. The bridle was missing a couple of rivets and the hames didn't have any straps nor chains, or collar. We tried the bridle on the mule. It had to be let out a little, but looked as if it would do. We went back to the house and Joe thanked Mr. Reeder.

"Hah!" he said. "Now you lazy, good for nothin' boys won't have no excuse for not workin', 'stead of galivantin' around all the time."

Joe and I headed on home. We tied the mule next to the little crib. Mama and the rest of the kids came out to see him. Pete grabbed a long stick.

"Goose him! Goose him!" he hollered. He jabbed at the mule with the stick.

Mike kicked, knocking the stick from Pete's hand and sending him tumbling. Pete hollered bloody-murder, more scared than hurt.

Mama clutched him, her face pale. "Now, you played whaley! Don't you never get behind that mule again. He'll kick out your brains. You're the beatenest kid I ever saw for wantin' to goose somethin' all the time." She dragged Pete, still hollering, towards the tent.

Opal, Betty, and Hazel kept a respectful distance from

the mule. "Will he bite? Can we ride him? What's his name?" Hazel asked, one question piled on top of another.

"Yes, he'll bite. No, you can't ride him. His name is Mike," Joe said.

I squinched my eyes and snorted the way Papa did. "You John Brown young uns, you aggravate a-body to death."

Hazel glared. "Oh, you think you're so smart. I'll gist spit on you and spit on you."

"You do and I'll tell Papa," I threatened.

Hazel backed down. Joe and I fed and watered the mule.

When Papa came in that night, he examined Mike's teeth by lantern light. "Well, he's no colt, but he's sound. He'll do 'til we can get us a young team. Tomorrow, I'll see 'bout findin' some more harness."

He set off on his mission right after breakfast and returned after dark. At the supper table, he reported, "Ovid Smith,* who works on the road, says he thinks he has an old collar big enough to fit that mule. Said I can have it and maybe a singletree. They was there on his place, when he moved there last year and he don't use 'em. I told him I'd send you boys over there to git 'em first thing tomorrow mornin', to lay 'em out."

Ovid Smith lived over by Rock Creek. I didn't relish another long walk so soon. "Can we ride the mule?" I asked.

Papa's black eyebrows bristled. "Ride the mule, your hindleg! He ain't no saddlehorse. He'll kill you. What's the matter with you John Brown young uns?"

We hadn't told Papa we had already ridden the mule. Joe nudged me under the table to keep quiet.

We got to Mr. Smith's about eight next morning. His two girls, Velma* and Marietta* came to the door.

---

*Names changed.

Joe took off his cap. "We're the Speer boys. We come for that harness Mr. Smith said Papa could have."

The girls glanced at each other.

"Well, Daddy went to work," Velma said, "and he said to tell you he couldn't find that stuff. He used to have it, but it's gone now." She didn't look directly at us as she talked.

The whole thing sounded fishy to me, but we couldn't dispute her words.

Joe put on his cap. "A'right, thank you anyway."

We walked back to the main road.

"What d'ya think?" I asked.

Joe spit on the ground. "Sounds funny to me."

We passed the Rock Creek store. Jess Haynes' team of little red ponies and wagon stood there. In a few minutes, Jess caught up with us, a tall, young man with a ruddy complexion.

"You want to ride?" His voice always boomed as if coming from the depths of his stomach.

"You betcha," I said.

Joe and I climbed onto the spring seat beside him. Jess and Pansy Reeder had gotten married. Jess asked where we had been. We told him about the mule and harness.

An odd look came into his eyes. "You know what? I was over by Ovid Smith's last night. I saw Lem Hatcher talking to him. I'll betcha a dollar, Hatcher told Ovid not to let you folks have that stuff."

Joe and I sat silent a moment. Joe shook his head. "I ain't lookin' forward to tellin' Papa 'bout this."

Dexter Welch Calvin, Okla.
now of McMinnville, Ore

Chapter 12

WE'LL NEVER BE HUNGRY AGAIN

"That no good, dad-gummed, black hearted scoundrel!" Papa exploded. "Someday, that Lem Hatcher's goin' to push me too far!" He slammed his big fist down on the table, sparks leaping in his black eyes.

The rest of us raised our voices in a babble, for anything that threatened Papa threatened us.

"You John Brown young uns!" Papa roared above the noise. "A-body can't hear it thunder!"

We hushed.

Papa squinched his eyes. "I knew in my own mind today, the way Ovid Smith acted, when he told me he couldn't find that stuff that he was lyin'."

"We knew those girls were, too," Joe said.

"Papa, why does Lem Hatcher keep doin' this?" I asked.

Papa looked grim. "He figgers if he can keep us from farmin' this land, he can have it without workin' for it."

Indignation churned within me. "You goin' to let him git by with it?" I didn't think Papa was a coward, but sometimes I wondered how he could keep from taking that old T-barker shotgun and filling Lem Hatcher full of buckshot.

Papa's barrel-chest heaved. "That's the trouble with tryin' to live by the Bible. The Lord sayeth, '*Vengeance is mine.'* But one of these days, if Lem Hatcher keeps on, I gist might help the Lord out a little."

That day couldn't come too soon for me. I'd like nothing better than to see Hatcher get what he deserved. I guess I wasn't as religious as Papa.

Mama looked scared. "Lem Hatcher ain't really hurt us."

Papa snorted. "No, but he's shore nibblin' us to death." He pulled off his worn shoes. "He ain't stoppin' me. I'll git us some harness some way."

I knew Papa would, once he made up his mind. Still, it bothered me that he kept taking this stuff off Hatcher. After Joe and I went to bed that night under the hickory tree, where we slept when the weather was hot, I rolled over towards him.

"Joe, do you think Papa's 'fraid of Lem Hatcher?"

Joe studied the stars a moment. "I don't 'magine. Papa's got all of us to look after. What would become of Mama and us if anything happened to Papa? Naw, there's more than one way to show courage."

Maybe so. Still, I wished Papa would go over there and beat the thunder out of that sneaking Lem Hatcher.

Things rocked on for a few days. Bill Lanham, an old Kentuckian, gave Papa a collar and a pair of trace chains. Alley Reeder let us have the irons off an old singletree. Papa cut a long pole and made a new singletree to fit the irons. Mr. Reeder gave us the old plow. Papa scrounged plow points from Alley Reeder. He sharpened them then set Joe and me to plowing with the mule.

The work proved harder than I thought. The new ground was full of rocks. Joe couldn't handle both the plow and reins at the same time, so I had to guide the mule while Joe handled the plow. We hooked a chain around the old logs and stumps. Mike strained and dug his feet in, pulling out the stumps.

When Papa had time, he went to the woods and cut

two hickory runners. He nailed some poles across them, making a sled. Now, we could haul stuff around the clearing. Mike didn't seem to mind the hard work.

One evening, Joe came in riding the mule. Papa stared in amazement.

"I didn't know that mule would ride!"

Joe grinned. "We rode him home the day we got him."

Papa digested this fact. "Well, he ain't no saddlehorse and we won't ride him much, but it's good to know we have somethin' we can ride once in awhile. Tag can ride him to Rock Creek in the mornin' to get coal-oil."

"I can?" I could hardly believe my good fortune.

"Yeah, maybe that way you won't play 'long the road so much and can git back to your work."

I might of known there was a catch to it.

Day after day, we worked in the hot August sun, straining to clear the new ground. One day, when we were hauling logs on the sled, Mike balked.

"Now, wait a minute," Papa cautioned. "Don't whip him. If you do, you'll ruin him. He'll git so he'll balk all the time and won't be any good."

We stood around about fifteen minutes waiting for the mule to move. It seemed like nonsense to me. When any of us kids balked, Papa knew how to cure us in a hurry with a switch. He exhibited a lot of patience now with the mule. At last, Mike decided to go on.

Papa grinned. "See? Now, you boys, if he ever does that again, gist stop and wait."

We didn't have to wait long. The next day, during Papa's absence, Joe and I were still hauling logs on the sled, when Mike balked again. We couldn't get him to do anything. After thirty minutes, I got exasperated.

"Joe, he ain't goin' to do nothin'. Let's whip him."

"No, Papa said not to."

"Joe, that mule's goin' to stand there all day and Papa's goin' to get mad at us 'cause this work's not done."

Joe nodded glumly. "But he said not to whip him. It would ruin him."

I studied on this a moment. "Then I know how to start him. Let's build a fire under him."

Joe brightened. "Yeah, that might work."

We gathered some twigs and built a little pile of wood beneath the mule. Mike batted his ears a couple of times and swung his head, trying to see around the blinders. Joe and I snickered in anticipation.

"Gist keep on a standin' there, you old fool," I said. "We'll fix you."

Joe lit the twigs. We fanned the flame into a blaze and fed it bigger sticks. As the heat increased, Mike's ears twitched. I could smell hair singeing. Mike stamped his feet and switched his tail. He leaned against the collar and moved forward.

"Oh, boy! We done it!" I exclaimed.

My joy proved short-lived. Mike stopped the sled directly over the fire. The flames curled up through the poles, threatening to engulf the whole thing.

I yelled in alarm. "If that sled burns, Papa'll git us for shore!"

Joe hollered at the mule and tried to drive him forward. I pulled on the bridle. Mike had his feet planted clear to China and didn't intend to move another step.

"Git that fire out from under the sled!" Joe said.

He grabbed a long stick and raked excitedly at the burning sticks under the sled.

When the danger was over, we looked at each other sheepishly.

"If Papa ever finds out, he'll skin our hides," Joe said.

"I won't tell if you won't," I promised.

We sat down to wait for the mule to go. After five minutes, evidently having decided he had taught us a lesson, Mike put his shoulder to the collar and plodded on across the clearing, dragging the sled.

Next day, Papa noticed the smoke-blackened poles. "What happened to that sled?"

"Oh, Mike may have dragged it too close to a burning log," Joe spoke in an off-handed manner.

"You want to be careful doin' that," Papa scolded. "You could burn that sled up that way."

"Yeah," Joe agreed.

September came, and with it the prospect of cooler weather and maybe rain. The cane, as Papa gazed out across it, looked stunted. It was a constant battle for us kids to keep the garden going, carrying water to it. We had dug the potatoes in July and Papa planted the little ones back for a fall crop. Watermelons, cantaloupes, and tomatoes still clung to the vines. Okra had to be picked every day. Papa had planted crowder peas and whipporwill peas in the corn and maize patches. He broadcast a fall turnip patch. We had sweet potatoes, winter squash, and pumpkins.

Mama's hens hatched out a dozen baby chicks. One by one, the varmints got them, then all but two of the big chickens. Papa suggested we might as well eat them before the varmints got them.

The pigs, calf, and cow were doing fine. March and Rex were settling down, outgrowing their puppy ways. I loved the clearing. I hoped we never went back to Tulsa.

Opal still hated the place. Everybody wondered why she didn't go to Sunday School with the rest of us kids. If anybody said anything to her, she burst into tears. She flared at the least little thing. She was getting so stubborn, even Mama couldn't do much with her. Loren and Raymond Reeder came over often to visit. I was sure it was to see Opal, but she always ran off and hid. Once, Loren told me he thought Opal was pretty and he would like to go with her. When I told Opal, she said she didn't want to go with any boys.

Sometimes, Bud and Eunice mailed us some magazines. Opal cut pictures of beautiful homes from them and kept them in a scrapbook at the bottom of the wardrobe. She threw a fit if anyone touched them. Occasionally, she would show them to Betty, who dreamed of a new house, too.

September moved along. Rex and March were trailing better. Sometimes, when I went after the cow, Rex would chase her. I scolded him for this. I tried to get off without him.

One evening, I been gone about thirty minutes trailing the cow, when I saw Rex coming. I hid. I could see his nose to the ground and tail ringing. He found me and jumped all over me. I scolded him and tried to send him back to the tent. He wouldn't go.

A week later, I heard Rex baying down by the spring. "He's got somethin' treed, Papa. Maybe it's somethin' 'sides a terrapin this time. Can I go see?"

Papa hesitated.

"It's about quittin' time," I urged. "On the way back, I can drag up a load of deadwood for Mama to cook supper with."

"Yeah," he agreed. "Go ahead."

I set off, happy to be getting out of work. Rex kept barking. I didn't hurry. I was sure it was a terrapin. When I reached the spring, I found Rex sitting on the ground, gazing up at a small hickory. I thought he'd treed one of the cats again. There sat a squirrel on a limb, twenty feet above the ground. My skin prickled. I was so tickled I couldn't see.

"Bring me a gun!" I hollered. "He's got a squirrel! Rex has got a squirrel!"

"Yaaa-hoooo!" Papa called back in the long, ringing tone we used as a signal in the woods.

I petted Rex and told him what a good dog he was. Shortly, Papa arrived with the shotgun and axe. March ran along behind him. She spotted the squirrel and bayed him, too.

"Papa, look up there what this old dog has found," I said, pointing.

Papa grinned. "Yeah, there he sits. Boy, it's a big un. Rex's goin' to make a shore 'nuff squirrel dog." He took a green shell from his pocket and slipped it into the shotgun.

"Papa, let me shoot him," I begged.

"Do you think you can do it?" he asked.

"Shore," I spoke confidently. I had never fired a shotgun, but Loren had let me fire his .22 a couple of times.

Papa handed the shotgun to me. "Don't let him git away. Now, gist look down the barrel and sorta aim at him. Don't miss him 'cause these shells are too hard to git. When you shoot, it's goin' to kick a little."

I knew all that, I thought. Impatiently, I opened the breech. The gun had been in the family a long time. Papa had traded a pig of Houston's for it, when Houston was a boy. Houston had left the gun with Papa, knowing he needed it worse than he. I slipped the shell into the right, short-range chamber, and sighted as if the shotgun were a .22. The squirrel scooted around the tree out of sight.

"I'll make him turn tree." Papa moved around the tree and rattled a bush.

The squirrel slid back to my side of the tree. I squeezed the trigger. The gun boomed and kicked back against my shoulder. The shot tore the squirrel in two and the pieces fell to the ground.

"Boy, you shore got him" Papa said, "but I didn't mean for you to blow him in two."

The dogs grabbed one part of the squirrel. I got it away from them. Papa let the dogs smell the squirrel and gave them the entrails.

Tickled, I petted Rex. "Good dog, good dog."

Papa examined the squirrel, trying to determine its

age. "Well, it's an old one," he decided. "Guess we can pick the shot out and have squirrel and dumplin's."

We started back to the house. The sun was going down.

"You'd better drag up some limbs," Papa reminded me.

All at once, I saw Rex take off, his nose to the ground and tail ringing. "Papa, he's after somethin' else!"

"Aw, he's probably gist smelled where I come down."

Rex went on about one hundred and fifty yards, then sat down at the foot of another tree and barked, his blabberlips and ears flopping. Papa and I hurried over there.

Papa's eyes widened in surprise. "Dad-gummed if he don't have two more half-grown squirrels treed up there."

I felt so proud of Rex, I was fit to burst. "We ain't never goin' to be hungry any more. We're goin' to be eating squirrel all the time!"

This tree was hollow and not much bigger than the other one. The squirrels ran inside the tree.

"Well, we can't waste all our shotgun shells on these." Papa laid down the gun. "Tag, climb up there and stop up that hole. We'll cut the tree down."

I climbed up and stuffed my shirt in the hole. We chopped down the tree. March and Rex whined and danced around, waiting for the squirrels to run out. Papa chopped a little hole about a foot below the knot in the tree. I could see the squirrels moving inside. Papa punched the squirrels around with a stick until he could get one of them by the tail.

"You gist goin' to pull him out?" I asked.

"You don't never gist pull one out," Papa corrected. "They's got long teeth, and they'll bite a hunk outa you. It'll hurt. I'm goin' to show you how to do a thing."

I stood back and watched. Papa got hold of the squirrel's hindlegs. The squirrel clawed at the tree. With a quick movement, Papa yanked him from the hole and hit his head against the tree. The squirrel went limp. Rex and March leaped on him. I got the squirrel away from them and petted Rex. Papa poked in the hole for the other squirrel.

I pressed eagerly, "Let me try that. Let me get that other one outa there."

Papa looked doubtful. "I'm tellin' you, you got to be quick and know what you're doin'."

I thought, 'Shoot, I can do anything you can, old man.' "I can do it," I begged.

"A'right," Papa agreed. "I'll let you try it. If you git bit, don't come cryin' to me."

"I won't get bit," I said, full of confidence.

I poked around in the hole with the stick until I could get hold of the squirrel's tail, the way Papa had done. Then, I got hold of one of the squirrel's hindlegs.

"I got him," I said.

"Now, jerk him out real fast and hit him quick," Papa said.

I jerked on the squirrel. Somehow, he kept holding on. I couldn't get him out of there. I wiggled him around and glanced at Papa, in embarrassment. Suddenly, the squirrel twisted around and nabbed me in the arm. I jerked my hand back, and threw him off. He took out running. About the third hop, Rex had him. My arm stung like a scorpion sting and blood dripped from the wound. I stood there, feeling foolish.

Papa looked at me, grinned a little, and shook his head. "Well, you'll learn."

We carried the squirrels home. Mama picked the shot out of the old one for dumplings. She fried the young squirrels, made a pan of biscuits, and milk gravy. We sat down to a fine meal.

"Boy, howdy," I said. "We got two real squirrel dogs now. We'll never want for anything to eat again."

How little did I know.

Chapter 13

PICKING COTTON

March never did seem blessed with much sense. Nor was she much of a hunter. Rex was the aggressive one who showed all the initiative. March liked to chase rabbits. This would spoil a good squirrel or opossum dog. I was afraid March would get Rex to chasing rabbits, too.

Rex and I had become real pals. About the only place I went that Rex didn't go was down to Uncle Bryan's fishing. We rambled in the woods and I became aware that Rex had grown up.

A great change had come over me, too. I was no longer a city boy. I'd learned things: how buzzards circled over something dead; where the fish fed; what berries were good to eat; how to sit and watch for a squirrel or rabbit to hop out. Rex and I had become hunters together. The dog was important to our livelihood.

Late one afternoon, Papa saw two rabbits nibbling at the peanuts, cutting the stalks off. "I know in my time I do git aggravated," he said. "First the owls et my chickens; now the rabbits are tryin' to eat the peanuts. If it ain't one John Brown thing it's another. Tag, I want you to go out there with March and chase them rabbits 'til you catch 'em. I don't want Rex goin', but March ain't much account for nothin' else. You hear?"

"Yes, sir, we'll git 'em."

Papa tied Rex to a hickory tree. I called March. We ran to the garden. I saw the rabbits at the end of the peanut row. Anything that destroyed the crop was destroying us, so this was serious business.

I threw a rock at the rabbits. "Sic 'em, March."

The rabbits bolted through the brush fence and into the woods, with March nipping at their heels. I followed. March ran the rabbits into a hollow log. I plugged the open ends with bark and sticks and hurried back to the tent.

"Papa, old March has got both rabbits in a holler log. What d'ya want me to do?"

"Well, Lord-a-mercy," Papa snorted in exasperation at my helplessness. "Git the axe and come on. We'll chop 'em out."

March still guarded the log, whining and dancing around.

Papa bent stiffly and peered inside the log. "Yeah, I see 'em, way back in there." He couldn't reach them. They wouldn't bite you like a squirrel.

I stood by with the axe. "You want me to chop a hole in it?"

Papa rocked back on his heels. "No, wait a minute. I'll show you how to git them rabbits outa there."

He cut a forked stick, about three-feet long, and poked around in the log until he touched one of the rabbits. He twisted the stick. The stick got tangled up in the rabbit's fur. Papa dragged him out and laid him across a log. I dispensed the rabbit with a quick blow of the axe. March danced around, eager for the rabbit.

"Shall we let her have it?" I asked.

"Aw, I guess," Papa said. "They's not fittin' to eat this time of year, poor and warty."

I got to looking. "Papa, this rabbit's not poor. Look how fat he is."

"Let me see that thing." Papa cut the rabbit open. The entrails were embedded in clean-looking fat. Papa stared in surprise. "Well, this is a good-lookin' rabbit. I believe we'll gist eat this little scamp."

We caught the other rabbit. He was fat, too. Mama fried them and made biscuits and gravy.

So, March was proving some worth, too. When she was around. She had come into her first heat this past week and would run off and stay a day or two at a time. I kept Rex tied so he wouldn't follow her.

Saturday at noon, I realized March had been gone three or four days. "Papa, I don't know where that dog is."

"Aw, she's probably gone off lookin' for a mate. She'll come home, when she gits ready."

I shook my head. "No, she always come back before this. I'm goin' to look for her."

"Do what you want to. We're goin' to rest this afternoon anyway. No tellin' where she is though."

Right after our noon meal, I untied Rex. He and I walked down by the spring and up past the bee tree. I listened, looked, and hollered for March. Rex and I circled south into Mossy Hollow and up the canyon, east toward Alley Reeder's. High in the sky, I saw buzzards circling above an old crib that stood in a field between Alley's and Buford McNutt's. Uneasy, I moved towards the crib. When I got near, I could smell something putrid. Rex sniffed around and whined.

The crib had once been Billy Hawkins' home. It sat on a rock foundation with a split-log floor. A wall and part of the flooring had caved in, but Alley had some hay stored there.

Rex scratched at an opening under the foundation, whined, and looked at me, pleading.

"What is it, boy? Is she under there?"

I flattened myself on the ground, and looked under the crib. Way at the back, some logs had fallen through the floor. One had March pinned beneath it. She was dead.

At the sight, I burst into tears, clutching Rex. True March hadn't proved much account, but I loved her anyway. Probably, she had chased a rabbit under the crib and knocked something lose. The logs fell on her.

I stumbled home. The other kids were as heartbroken as I, when they heard of March's death. Even worse, we had lost part of our means of livelihood. I was glad it hadn't been Rex. He was a much better dog. I loved him all the more after that and wondered if dogs had a heaven.

September mellowed. Smoke curled lazily into the sky. The woods turned red and yellow. The cotton ripened. Mr. Goodman sent word his crop was ready to pick. Papa told Joe, Opal, Betty, and I to go down there to work to pay for the mule.

Mama packed us a lunch of fried potatoes and biscuits in a half-gallon syrup bucket. We took our white ducking cotton-sacks, which Mama had made on her sewing machine, and left at daylight.

Annie, Ed, and A.G. Goodman worked with us. Mr. Goodman always claimed he was too sick to work much himself.

The work was hard. We had to bend over all the time, or crawl, dragging the cotton-sacks. The sharp-pointed bolls pricked our fingers. Joe picked two rows at a time while Betty, Opal, and I each one. At the end of our rows, Mr. Goodman weighed the sacks. Joe tallied the weights with a metal-capped, indelible lead pencil in a little yellow book with "Garret Snuff" written on the cover. I stood in the wagon, emptying the sacks. Sometimes, when Mr. Goodman wasn't watching, I left a little cotton in my sack to start back on.

At noon, we ate our lunch, looked over the weights,

and went back to work. We felt so tired, we could scarcely drag ourselves home each night.

On his days off, Papa picked cotton with us. It amazed me how fast he was. He had a way of reaching out and keeping a steady stream of cotton flowing into that bag.

We spent five days at Mr. Goodman's, earning about fifteen dollars. October filled the sky. I had been wondering about something.

"Papa, school's goin' to start again the first of November. You reckon we might could go?"

I wanted desperately to do so. "Son, learn all you can," Mama said often. "You can lose your money but learning stays with you." I knew Papa didn't see much need for school. Too much education put foolish notions in "a-body's" head that they wouldn't have to work for a living, he thought. I knew there was a whole world out there waiting to be explored. I longed to know why gun powder exploded; how a radio talked; why an iron ship floated; what the moon was made of. I waited with bated breath for Papa's answer. He could say no very easily.

He scratched his head. "I been thinkin' about that. I need you here on the clearin', but the law says you got to go to school. You need clothes though. Maybe you can pick cotton for somebody else to earn some clothes. I'll ask around at work, see if I can find you a job."

New clothes *and* school. I felt dizzy at the prospect. Joe thought he was too big for the seventh grade now, but the idea of new clothes sounded fine.

Papa found us a job picking cotton for Bill Lanham. After that, we picked for Jess Haynes, Earl Lane, Virgil Gould, and Mr. Cross, who lived in the bottoms by Lem Hatcher.

At night, we studied the Montgomery Ward catalog, trying to decide what we were going to order. When the time came, Mama filled out the order blank by lamplight, each of us sitting beside her, telling her what we wanted.

I chose two sweet-potato colored flannel shirts, a red corduroy cap with ear flaps, a pair of split-cowhide shoes, two pair of overalls, two pair of underwear, two pair of wool socks, and a whipcord jacket. All this cost a staggering seven dollars.

Joe ordered a pair of dark brown dress shoes, a sweet-potato shirt, a white one for church, khaki jacket, overalls, socks, and underwear. Mama ordered each of the girls a dress, material for another, shoes, coats, and petticoats. She also bought some "silk" underwear for Opal, and a sweet-potato shirt, cowhide shoes, overalls, and a brown leather cap for Papa.

Pete couldn't understand why Mama wouldn't write his order down too. His coveralls were full of holes. Mama tried to explain that he and she didn't need anything. They weren't going anywhere. The rest of us had to have clothes for school and work, and we had earned the money. Pete didn't understand and burst into tears. Watching him, I felt guilty about all the things I had ordered.

Joe glanced up from the book he was reading. "Mama, why don't you take that white shirt of mine off and order Pete something. I kinda wanted it, but I don't have to have it."

"No," Papa interfered. "You earned that money. You need clothes for meetin' and I like for you to go. Larie, take my shoes off instead. I can mend these old uns a little, maybe tack some more leather on the soles."

His worn brogans should have been thrown away long ago. What held them together was anybody's guess.

"No," Mama stated firmly. "You need them shoes. These have been mended too many times already. They ain't helpin' your bad feet any. Pete'll just have to understand. He can't have anything. There ain't enough money."

Pete wailed louder. We all felt bad. Mama needed things, too. After a moment, Papa got up and walked outside, blinking rapidly.

Next morning, Papa placed the money for our order in a tobacco sack and tied it to Joe's overalls. "Don't lose it."

Joe walked down to the mailbox to meet Tommy George, the mail carrier, to buy a money order and send our letter. We kids started looking for our order back the next day.

Papa shook his head. "You young uns do beat all. It'll be two-three weeks at the earliest before them clothes git here."

Even so, we hoped some miracle might occur. Each day, one of us ran down to the mailbox to see.

I strutted around, bragging. "I'm goin' to have me some swell duds, when our order comes in."

Papa waved his hand. "You'll play hob if you don't keep pullin' them peavines."

A week passed. School started.

I fretted impatiently. "Boy, howdy! How long is it going to take for our clothes to come? I believe they lost that order; or they've gist kept our money. If they have, we'll have 'em put in jail."

Joe laughed. "How you going to have Montgomery Ward put in jail?"

"Well, I don't know, but I'll do somethin'!"

"Montgomery Ward is a big company. They's thousands of people work there."

"Well, I'll gist put 'em all in jail."

Hazel placed her hand on her hip. "If they don't send me my new dress purty soon, I'm goin' to spit on 'em."

Betty laughed. "Yeah, you'd fly, too, if you had wings."

The first frost came, killing the garden. We turned the sow and pigs out to eat what was left and to root for hickory nuts and acorns in the woods.

A few days later, at suppertime, Rex began barking. I

saw a familiar figure limping through the gate with a suitcase. "Perry's home!"

We all tumbled out of the tent to greet him with a babble of voices. Where had he been? What had he been doing? How was his heel? Did he find work?

Yes, he had worked a little. He had been staying with Avis and Charley McClure. He had the cast off his heel, but couldn't walk as well as he could before his accident. He had a pair of dimestore glasses and was home to stay for awhile.

Mama's face shone. She was pleased to have Perry home. While we ate, he caught us up on the news of the other kids in Tulsa. Herman and Albert were driving taxicabs. Charley McClure was barbering, but taking in more credit than anything else. Virgil Grey was getting rich to hear him tell it, but Vesta said they were starving. Not much use in Frank going to Tulsa. Jobs were still scarce though things might be a little better because of the "made work," under Roosevelt.

We, in turn, caught Perry up on the news of the clearing. We told him about ordering new clothes, all but Mama and Pete.

Perry opened his suitcase. "I got some new duds." He showed us a spiffy pair of bell-bottomed trousers, yellow polo shirt, and brown leather shoes wrapped in paper.

His suitcase had a heavenly smell of far away places, Rose Hair Oil, and shoe polish. "Can I have some of that hair oil?" I asked.

He shut the suitcase. "Nope, that's mine."

He gave Pete and each of the girls a stick of gum and Joe a pack of Camels. He handed me a sample tube of toothpaste, "Ipana, the Smile of Beauty." I never found out whether it helped my smile. That Ipana tasted so good, I ate it all.

Perry handed Mama four one dollar bills. "Mama, this is all I got, but I want you to take it and order you and Pete something, too."

Mama's eyes glistened with tears.

Pete flung himself against Perry. "P-Perry, you my b-buddy some more!"

Papa grinned. He and Perry did not always get along. In some ways, Perry might be tight, but in others he could be generous. "Son, I know this money didn't come easy, but it couldn't have come at a better time."

The following evening, Frank came home for good, the cow paid for. It seemed like a real homecoming, all of us together again.

"Now, we got lots of help with the cane," I said.

Next day, we all worked together. Papa had borrowed two long cane knives from Mr. Reeder. I had a thin board with a handle on it. With these, we stripped the leaves off the cane stalks and tied the leaves in bundles.

Perry couldn't get around in the field too well. He stacked the bundles in the crib. For some reason, he liked to cut wood. In the late afternoon, he did chores around the tent and cut wood. Not just enough wood for one night, but for two or three.

"No use cuttin' just a little bit at a time," he reasoned. "When I come in at night tired, I'd rather sit down and rest."

Opal and I happily let him take over the wood cutting chore.

In two days, we had the cane stripped. Next, came the heading and cutting. Finally, we hauled the stalks to the sorghum mill to be squeezed for sorghum molasses.

There were two sorghum mills in the community, Bill Lanham's, two and one half miles away, and Mr. Ellison's, over by Rock Creek.

Each mill was an old press type, with two big iron gears and rollers driven by a long pole attached to a mule that walked around the mill. The mill operator fed the cane stalks into the rollers. The rollers crushed the cane into "pumies," and the juice ran down a spout into a pan. The operator poured the juice into a long pan and set the pan over the fire to boil. He skimmed the debris and scum off the top. He stirred the juice until it thickened.

Sometimes, Mr. Lanham got in a hurry and burned his syrup, or let it boil too long and it turned sugary. Mr. Ellison, who was a hard-shell Baptist preacher, always made good syrup. Papa contracted with Mr. Ellison to take our cane for ten percent.

Mr. Lanham had given us the mule collar and let us pick cotton for him. Now, he was letting us pasture old Mike over on his place free of charge. We were through with the mule for now, but could not turn him out like Roady, for he would run off. Papa hated doing Mr. Lanham this way, for he was good to us, but said he could not risk having the molasses ruined.

Getting someone to haul the cane to the mill proved another matter. We could not use Mike as we did not have a wagon and it was too far for the sled. The Reeders had their team and wagon tied up, hauling cotton and cane. Papa asked Fred Doyle, offering a gallon of molasses a load, the equivalent of fifty cents. One could haul three loads a day, which wasn't bad pay. Fred Doyle said no. Oscar Elwood said the cane was stunted and would not be worth hauling. Finally, Papa contracted with John Overton to haul the cane for a tenth of it. He promised to be at the clearing first thing Monday morning.

We kids hurried to get the cane ready. By Monday noon, John Overton had not shown up.

"Maybe we better hold up cuttin' any more cane and go see if he's comin'," Frank said, in charge now while Papa was at work. "If that cane don't get to the mill soon after it's cut, it'll ruin."

He sent Joe and me over to Overton's. John's bare feet stuck out from under the old car he was working on. When he saw us, his long thin frame slid out from under the car.

Joe said, "We come to see if you are goin' to haul our cane?"

"Well, I'll tell you." John paused to spit. "I got to talking to Oscar Elwood and some of 'em. They said it wouldn't pay to haul that cane. I decided not to do it. I figgered, when I didn't show up, you'd know I wasn't coming."

Joe eyed him a moment, then turned abruptly, and we left.

Back at the clearing, we told Frank what Joe Overton had said. Later, we repeated our tale to Papa, when he came in.

Papa's eyes squinched. "If this ain't a purty come off! Now we're apt to lose that cane."

Chapter 14

THE RAT KILLING

No one said anything for a moment. The cold November wind snapped the tent sides. The orange lamplight flickered across Papa's stubby whiskers. It seemed to me that he had aged a lot this past year. Gray streaked his black hair and deep lines etched his face like a wagon track. His chest heaved.

"Well, it can't be helped," he said at last. "Tomorrow, I'll see if I can find somebody else to haul that cane."

Frank went with him. They asked all over the neighborhood, even asked Buford McNutt. Buford said his team was busy, though Papa said it didn't appear to be.

Papa didn't know where else to ask. He and Frank started home. By our mailbox, they met Jim Rackley driving a team of mules and wagon. A tall, thin man with sparse white hair, Mr. Rackley lived south of Lem Hatcher. Everybody made fun of the Rackleys, saying they were hillbillies. I didn't see how they could be any more so than the rest of us. Mr. Rackley worked part-time on the WPA too. He had been to Rock Creek store and stopped to talk a minute. He asked if Papa had got his cane hauled? Papa said no and told him what happened.

Mr. Rackley said, "Mr. Speer, I got two boys over thar. They ain't doing nothin', and my team ain't busy. We'll hep you haul that cane. You don't have to pay us nuther. You gist tell us when."

The Lord had answered Papa's prayers again, I thought, when Papa told us about this.

First thing Wednesday, Mr. Rackley's two sons were at the clearing as promised. They jumped right in, helping us haul that cane. Papa paid Mr. Rackley a gallon a load though Mr. Rackley protested.

Papa insisted. "I'm an honest man and I always pay my debts."

Mr. Ellison received his share, too. We ended up with about forty gallons of sorghum molasses for ourselves. Not quite as much as Papa had estimated, but he felt satisfied.

The next day, Mr. Lanham sent word for us to get Mike out of his pasture. He said he did not have enough grass for him. I guess he was angry about us taking our cane to Mr. Ellison. You couldn't blame him; still business was business.

That afternoon, Papa came home from work early. The WPA supervisor had laid him off. He said the project had run out of money. The first big rain that fall had washed the dam out anyway.

Now, with winter setting in, being without a job was something else to worry about. We had two extra mouths to feed, too. We had plenty of canned food and vegetables in the root cellar. Roady still gave milk; the pigs would be ready to butcher soon as it turned a little colder. Squirrels, rabbits, and opossum lived in the woods. Papa thought we could make it until spring.

Rats infested the cribs though, eating the cane heads, corn, and goose-neck maize. The rats nested in the hay and burrowed into the dirt floor under the bundles and peavine hay.

"Boys," Papa said one evening, "them rats are a ruinin' that feed. We barely got enough to do our stock this winter as it is."

"What d'ya want us to do, Papa?" Joe asked.

"I don't care, but somehow, I want you to git rid of them rats. Ever' last one of 'em."

Frank's eyes gleamed. "I know, Papa, we could have us a real rat killin'. We'll git Albert, Loren, and J.W."

Joe caught his excitement. "They've got that feist dog. He's a natural-born rat killer, and we have Rex."

"J.W.'s got his bean flip, too," I added eagerly. "He hardly ever misses with that thing."

Papa glanced at the sky. "Do what you want. Tomorrow is Saturday, and it looks like rain. Might as well be doin' that as somethin' else. I want ever' one of them rats killed."

"We'll git 'em," Frank promised.

We talked over our plans for the rat killing that night. I'd been stewing all week because our catalog order still hadn't come and we couldn't go to school. This gave me something else to think about.

The following morning broke drizzly and gray. Frank and I walked over to the Reeders', Rex trotting along beside us. Perry had walked down to Uncle Bryan's for the weekend. Frank and I shivered in our thin jackets.

"I wish my new jacket would hurry up and come," I said.

"Yeah," Frank muttered.

I glanced at his long face, sorry I had mentioned the jacket. He had worked for Mr. Romine for six months and hadn't gotten a dime for himself. He was as threadbare as the rest of us. I knew it embarrassed him to go to church and see Leota the way his clothes looked.

Albert opened the door. "What're you peckerwoods up to?" he greeted.

"Come to see if you could help us do a little rat killin'. They're tryin' to clean out our cribs," Frank said.

Albert squinted in near-sightedness. "Why I 'spect we would. We'll do it if it harelips ever' cow in Texas!"

Loren grinned. "Gist let me and that little feist at them gentlemen."

J.W. scrambled for the door. "I'll be ready soon as I load my pocket with flint rocks."

Mr. Reeder sat by the fire, feeling poorly. "Aw, you sorry lookin' boys. If ya ain't out chasin' girls, you're out chasin' rats. Ya orta be out choppin' wood, doin' something useful."

"Now, Mr. Reeder," Mrs. Reeder chided. "Them boys work hard. They need to play a little, too."

We walked back to the clearing, the dogs taking the lead through the bare woods. Suddenly, Rex sat down at the foot of a big hickory tree and began baying.

My heart jumped. "He's got somethin'. Old Rex has got a squirrel!"

J.W. whipped a stone from his pocket. "Let me git him." Snaking his tongue out of the corner of his mouth, he leveled the bean flip and cut down on the squirrel. The squirrel tumbled from the tree, hit dead center. Rex pounced on him.

I grabbed the squirrel from Rex. "Looky there! A big old fat squirrel for dinner. I told you Rex was a real squirrel dog!"

We proudly carried the squirrel home. Mama clapped her hands, pleased to see it. "I was wonderin' what I was going to cook for dinner."

We went to the cribs. Papa and Joe had the axe and two sharp hickory sticks with which to club the rats.

"You'll have to move all the shocks outa the cribs and dig them rats outa them holes in the dirt floor," Papa directed. "Then we'll have to fix them holes in the walls and door so them rats can't git back in."

Albert strutted forward. "We'll get rid of them little dudes for you, Mr. Speer. Don't you worry none."

Joe and Frank climbed into the crib. Albert and Loren took up the clubs, and I got the hoe. Papa stood back with the axe. J.W. stationed himself between the crib and brush fence.

"Let 'em go!" Albert hollered.

Joe and Frank moved a bundle. Two big rats ran out the door. The feist nabbed one and shook it, breaking its back. Rex looked a little puzzled. He had never killed a rat. Game, he jumped the second one. The rat twisted in his grip and bit his nose. Rex turned loose with a howl. The rat fled towards Albert. Albert swung and missed. The rat veered towards the brush fence.

I hopped up and down, excitedly. "Git him, Jay! Git him!"

J.W. whooped and let fly with another rock. The rat tumbled end over end. The dogs got him, and we cheered.

Each time Joe and Frank moved a bundle, more rats ran out, fat on our hard-earned grain. Rex had learned his lesson quickly. He grabbed the rats right in the back and popped them in two.

"Get 'em, Rex!" I encouraged.

Loren swung his club. "Run them gentlemen this way."

"Sic 'em, feist!" Albert said.

Papa stood back grinning. Mama and the girls watched a bit. Pete ran forward with a long stick.

"Goose 'em! Goose 'em," he hollered.

J.W. had an excellent spot between the crib and brush fence. Those rats that got past the rest of us and the dogs, J.W. got with his bean flip.

Papa tossed the dead rats into a tub. "That's thirty-four. Clean 'em outa there, boys."

Joe and Frank moved some of the bundles in the crib outside. They gouged sharp sticks into the holes in the dirt floor, scareing out more rats. The morning had warmed. By one o'clock, when we got the first crib cleaned out, we were all sweaty, dirty, and blood-splattered. We stood around the tubsful of rats, laughing and talking, while the dogs rested nearby.

Albert squinted at the rats. "How many of them peckerwoods we got now, Mr. Speer?"

"Eight-seven." Papa was enjoying himself as much as the rest of us. "If I could shoot a bean flip good as J.W., I wouldn't need a shotgun."

J.W. looked bashful. "Ain't hard. All you got to do, Mr. Speer, is gist draw back and look where you're shooting. Usually, I try to knock their eyes out."

"Well, they're shore thick as fleas in there," Loren commented.

Frank grinned. "Ain't that the truth, oh, by dolly."

We went to the tent and ate dinner, still talking about the rats.

"Boy, that was the most fun I've had since the hogs et up my little brother," J.W. said.

Papa shoved back his chair. "You got plenty more chance. About half them rats run under that other crib."

"Hot dog!" J. W. rose. "Gist wait'll I git me some more ammunition."

I went with him down to the spring to help him load up on flint rocks. We returned to the cribs. The little one had a wooden floor. The door sagged on its hinges.

"Papa, let's take that door off," Frank suggested. "I can fix it later."

Papa nodded. "Do what you want to."

Frank wrapped his arms around the door to pull it off the hinges. A rusty nail on the backside jabbed him in the right arm. The wound looked blue and bled a little.

"You better get that seen about," Joe suggested.

"Aw, it's a'right," Frank dismissed. "I might miss some of the fun. I'll doctor it when we get through." He wrapped the rag he carried for a handkerchief around his arm. "Okay, let's go. Who's goin' to help me inside?"

"I will," Loren volunteered. "How 'bout us workin' that feist in there, too?"

"Suits me," Joe said.

He climbed into the crib. "I'll move bundles."

They set to work. The feist pounced on every rat he could. Those that got outside, Rex and the rest of us got them. When we were through, we had one hundred and thirty-six rats, two tubsful.

J.W. grinned in satisfaction. "Man, I wish I had a rat killin' to go to ever'day."

We dumped the dead rats in the woods. The Reeders headed for home. Papa, Joe, Frank, and I fixed the holes in the cribs. Frank cut some new leather hinges for the door and hung it back in place. His arm hurt a little. He showed the wound to Mama, that evening.

She frowned in concern. "You ought to have tended to that as soon as you done it." She washed the wound, poured coal-oil on it, and tied a clean rag around his arm.

The next day, Frank's arm seemed all right, but then it began to get sore. Mama looked worried.

"Gettin' hurt on a rusty nail can be bad," she said. "A-body can get blood poisonin'."

Frank shrugged. "Aw, Mama, it'll be a'right."

But by the fourth day, the skin around the wound had turned red. The redness spread. The wound came to a head like a blood boil. Frank paced the floor in pain.

Mama grieved for him. "Son, I got nothing to give you for the pain – not even aspirin."

She bathed his arm in hot salts water and applied a bread and milk poultice to draw out the poison. Papa made a poultice out of red oak bark and applied that. Nothing helped. Frank could scarcely stand the pain. Knots swelled up under his arm and on his neck. For three days and nights, he could not sleep.

Mama drew Papa aside. "Henry, that boy's got blood

poisonin'. It's gettin' all through him. If we don't do something, he'll die!"

A chill passed through me at her words.

Papa's brow furrowed. "We got no money for a doctor, no way to git him to town if we did."

"What're we goin' to do?" Mama whispered in fear.

Papa's face tightened. "I'll lance it myself."

He sharpened his pearl-handled pocketknife until the point was razor-sharp like a saber. He cut a wooden thread spool in two and stuck the knife blade through one half. The blade protruded an inch beyond the spool.

"This'll keep the blade from goin' too deep," he said.

Frank paced the floor. "Papa, I don't know if I can bear for you to lance it."

"If we had somethin' to deaden the pain – we got to lance it, we got no choice. If we had some liquor – " Papa felt in his pocket. "I got a quarter. I'll go down to Lem Hatcher and see if I can git some whiskey."

During his absence, Frank continued his pacing, his eyes wild with fever. The rest of us kids huddled on the bed.

"Is Frank goin' to die?" Hazel whispered.

"I don't know," I whispered back.

She went to Frank and petted him. "It'll be a'right, Rusty, Papa'll fix it."

I stumbled from the tent, my throat tight. I flung myself down under a hickory tree, hot tears streaming down my cheeks. Frank couldn't die. He and I were buddies. He helped Mama and Papa, all of us.

"Please, God, don't let him die!" I pleaded.

Rex came over, whined and lapped at my wet cheeks, trying to comfort me.

Papa returned, looking grim. "Lem Hatcher wouldn't sell me no whiskey. Said he didn't have any. Probably figgered I was tryin' to git some evidence against him." He turned to Frank. "Well, whiskey or no, we've got to lance that arm."

Frank nodded in dull resignation. "Where do you want me?

Papa motioned. "On the bed."

Frank laid down. Papa moved a cane-bottomed chair to the side of the bed. He laid a board across the chair. "I'll need ever'body's help."

We got around the bed as Papa directed, Perry and I on the left, Joe and Mama on the right, Betty, Hazel, and Opal at Frank's feet.

Papa picked up the knife and spool. "Okay, ever'body hold him. Frank, grit your teeth and turn your head."

Frank closed his eyes and clenched his teeth. Papa raised the blade. For a moment, it glistened in the light, then plunged into Frank's arm. Yellow pus flew. Frank screamed and thrashed in torment.

"Hold him!" Papa said.

We struggled with Frank. Papa wiped the pus off the wound with a clean rag, and pressed the tender flesh to get out the poison. Frank screamed again. Sweat beaded his forehead and his face looked pale as the winter moon.

"Sorry, boy, somethin' had to be done." Papa nodded at Mama.

She washed the wound with warm water, poured coal-oil on it, and bound it with clean rags. Frank gritted his teeth in pain.

Papa nodded in understanding. "Cry if you need to, son. Sometimes a man needs to cry."

Frank cried, great gulping sobs that released his tension. In a few minutes, he dropped into an exhausted sleep. The rest of us waited, not knowing if he would live or die.

Frank slept all evening. Mama cooled his head with wet clothes and bathed his arm.

Papa read his Bible, his lips moving: "*Man born of woman is of few days and full of trouble . . . .*"

I went to bed, fearing what might happen during the

night. When I awoke next morning, Mama still sat beside Frank.

"How is he?" I whispered, fearing the worst.

Mama looked exhausted. "Better. His fever's dropping."

I sank back on my pillow, relieved.

Frank slept until mid-morning. When he opened his eyes, the feverish look had gone. He grinned a little. "I'm weak as a cat, but I feel better."

The swelling had gone down and the red streaks were fading from his arm.

"You're goin' to be a'right," Mama said.

She kept him in bed for two days. The rest of us returned to our work. I had a chance to think again about our new clothes and school. Three weeks had passed since we had sent our order. I was beginning to think the post office had lost it, but when I went to the mailbox that Saturday, several packages hung on the mailbox. I ran with them all the way back to the clearing.

"Our order's in! Our new clothes come in!"

We tore excitedly into the packages. My new jacket was not among the contents. It was on back order. Everything else looked fine though.

Joe cocked his new cap on the back of his head and struck a pose. "Now, look youse mugs, I'm James Cagney, see?"

I buttoned the collar of my new sweet potato colored shirt and pulled my new red corduroy cap down over my forehead the way Harley and Clifford Lane wore theirs. "Uh, look at me. I'm from the country."

Joe howled with laughter. Frank sat on the bed. He got up and stumbled outside. I knew he was wondering how he was going to get new clothes of his own.

Chapter 15

TROUBLE AT SCHOOL

We wore our new clothes to Sunday School next morning, eager to show them off. Some of the other kids asked where we got them and how much we had to pay.

"Oh, three or four hundred and five," Joe responded, noncommittal.

Perry's eyes flashed, his answer more direct. "The same as you give for yours."

It was that time of year, when everybody sported new clothes, after they sold their cotton and school started. Albert Reeder had a new pair of high-topped yellow shoes. He wore a yellow silk tie with a knot in it that looked big as a biscuit and had a "diamond" stickpin in it. Loren had on a new white shirt with striped overalls, and J.W. a red shirt and black boots.

Eagerly, I told J.W., "We git to go to school tomorrow."

He wagged his head in dreary contemplation. "You can have my part."

Sunday School took up. Harlan Hull led off in prayer, then the young people, who always sat on the front row, led in singing. Will Davis reported on finances. Will sort of ran the church. His father, old "Uncle" Ed Davis, had deeded twenty acres here for a church and school, thirty years ago.

We broke up into classes, one in each corner of the

one-room church. Gloe McNutt taught my class. For some reason, Billy Hawkins and his wife invariably sat in the little kids class. Each Sunday, Billy dropped a buffalo nickel into the collection plate. When asked how many chapters he had read in the Bible, he shook his head. His wife reported how many chapters she had read.

Billy said, "Him read aloud to me. Do that count?"

After Sunday School, church took up. This Sunday, it was Tooley Green's turn to preach. The first Sunday of the month, Brother Ellison preached, but he being Baptist, didn't many stay to hear him. Dave Hutchinson and Arthur McKnight split the other two Sundays.

Tooley Green's bald head shone. He wore yellow garters to keep his shirt sleeves up, and yellow suspenders with a belt. He led in his favorite song: "*This world is not my home, I'm just a passing through . . .*"

He began his sermon, shouting in his high-pitched voice: "You gotta be born of the spurit and of the flash. The spurit is willin', but the flash is weak . . . ."

My mind drifted. I'd heard his message before. As I looked over the crowd, I thought everyone looked nice in their new clothes. I wished Frank had some. He had not come today because he still felt weak from the blood poisoning. Leota Ritter looked lonesome as she sat by herself in her new green dress.

After church, we walked back with the Reeders. At our mailbox, we turned the corner, then heard a wagon coming up the main road.

"Wait a minute, let's see who it is," I urged.

In a few moments, Mr. Rackley pulled up beside us. "Gist the ones I were lookin' fer. I got some cotton bolls that need pullin' and was wonderin' if anybody o'er your place could hep me? Three or four day's work. I'll pay."

I glanced anxiously at Joe. "Hazel, Betty, and I gotta go to school tomorrow."

Joe motioned to Perry. "Come over here a minute."

He and Perry whispered together, then came back.

"Mr. Rackley," Joe said, "we'll take that job. Be there first thing in the morning, if it's okay with Papa."

"Much obliged," Mr. Rackley said. "Be expectin' you."

We walked on. Joe and Perry grinned like a couple of opossums in a persimmon tree.

"What's up?" I asked.

"We're goin' to pick them bolls and give the money to Frank for some new clothes," Perry explained.

My heart swelled. Like Tooley Green had said, "the spurit is willin'," but in this case so was the "flash."

The news tickled Frank, and he insisted on helping though still weak.

"I'll go, too," Papa said. "Frank helped us, now we can help him."

With that settled, I looked forward to school with a clear conscience. Next morning, I hurried through my chores and got ready to go.

Opal sat down in a chair. "I ain't goin'."

Mama brushed Hazel's hair. "But, Opal, you got to go. The schoolboard's already onto your daddy again 'bout you kids not goin'. You don't go, the truant officer'll be down here after you."

Opal's eyes blazed. "I ain't goin'! I ain't never goin' to school again!" She grabbed her coat and fled to the woods.

Mama's lips trembled. Papa and the older boys had already left for Mr. Rackley's. Mama didn't know what to do.

"You want me to go after Opal?" I asked.

"No, it wouldn't do no good. I can't make her go. You others go along or you'll be late."

She handed me our lunch, some fried potatoes and biscuits in a half-gallon syrup bucket. I didn't see Opal any place, when we left the clearing. She was getting more peculiar all the time. She was bigger than Mama now, and Mama couldn't handle her any more.

It was cold. I wished I had my new jacket. We met J.W. and Zenora at the mailbox. Both were in the seventh grade. J.W. had his bean flip hanging around his neck.

I pointed. "They let you take that in?"

He grinned. "I always hide it outside someplace, then git it after school. I feel nekid without it."

Bohannon School sat on a hill a quarter-mile west of Bohannon Church. The church used to be the school, but there had been problems with the drinking water seeping into the cistern from the graveyard across the road. The church and school had been named for Lucy B. Bohannon, a Choctaw Indian who was allotted two sections of land here, when Indian Territory was broken up.

Inside the school, a partial partition divided the building into two classrooms. Cleburn Pounds taught grades one through four, and Charley Watson five through eight. Hazel went on Mr. Pounds' side; Betty and I on Mr. Watson's, along with J.W. and Zenora.

A wood-burning heating stove, with a tin shield behind it, heated the classroom. Mr. Watson's desk stood on a small stage before the students. An American flag, a clock, and picture of "The Last Trail" hung on the wall. I could smell chalkdust mingled with that of fried meat as Betty and I took our seats. Everyone stared at us.

Mr. Watson, wearing his yellow vest and blue serge suit, called the roll then turned his attention to me. "Willard Speer, what grade are you in?"

"Seventh," I fudged a little. That was the grade I would have been in had we gone to Amber the full year and to Bohannon this past spring and summer.

"Well, let's find out. Let's see how well you read." Mr. Watson handed me an American history book.

I knew I wouldn't have trouble here. I read a lot at

home and the family often discussed the things we read. I began reading without stumbling over the words.

Mr. Watson looked surprised, but pleased. "Well, Willard, let's see how you are in arithmetic."

He sent me to the board and gave me some problems. I worked them without any trouble. Then he tested me for Geography. I knew my stuff here. The school in Tulsa had been more advanced than Bohannon. I had listened to Perry and Frank talk about the places where they had hoboed. Often at night and on rainy days, we kids played a guessing game: What's the capital of Texas? What is Chicago noted for? What's the biggest farming valley in California?

Mr. Watson nodded. "You're doing all right. I guess you can be in the seventh."

I took my seat next to J.W. with a grin.

Betty did equally well. Mr. Watson put her in the fifth grade. Beyond the partition, I heard Hazel tell Mr. Pounds she was in the second grade. She had started in the first at Amber. Real smart, she had learned to read and write from the funny papers.

Mr. Watson only had sixty hours of college credit and was continuing his education in summer school at East Central State. During the reading class that morning, Leon McNutt paused, when he came to the word "magician."

"Maa-ji-cun," Mr. Watson prompted.

Betty's hand shot up. "Mr. Watson, that's incorrect. It's pronounced 'muh-gee-shun.'"

Mr. Watson turned red. "I was just telling him that to see if he knew," he spoke angrily, trying to cover his embarassment.

From that moment, I knew we were in trouble with Mr. Watson. The other students envied our book ability. In addition, we were squatters living in a tent, and Papa had closed off the road to Pine Spring. We were of a different religion, and Papa spoke out on his views.

At recess, George Lanham, sixteen and in the fifth grade, jumped me, saying Papa had said Mr. Lanham didn't make good syrup. Harold McNutt, in the sixth grade but bigger than I, and Sanford, in the fifth grade, jumped me, too. They told me Papa said Buford wouldn't let us borrow his team during cane harvest because Lem Hatcher had talked him out of it.

Mr. Watson broke up that squabble, but at noon, someone brought out a pair of boxing gloves. When someone new came to school, the boys wanted to decide the pecking order first thing. Everyone wanted to box with me.

I had always been a little husky for my age, but I didn't like fighting. If Papa found out, he would get me when I got home. I backed off. "No, I don't want to fight."

"Coward! Coward! Buttermilk soured!" the boys taunted.

I relented and put on the gloves with George Gould, a tall, good-looking blond boy in the seventh grade. Right off, instead of this being a boxing match like I'd seen in Tulsa once, I could see this was going to be an out and out fight to see if George could whip me.

I ducked his first blow and sidestepped a second one. Then, George landed a good one in my left eye. I shook my head, dazed for a moment. Anger flooded through me. I sailed into George and landed a solid blow on his nose. Blood flew. The teachers stopped the fight.

George seethed with anger. When the teachers walked away, he said, "Meet me after school and we'll finish this fight."

"No," I said. "We weren't fighting. We were only boxing. That was play."

"Coward! Coward!" the boys hollered again.

Harold McNutt jeered. "You wait, squatter. We'll get you after school. We'll take your clothes off and make you fight."

I swallowed. Harold was a huge guy, a regular bully.

J.W. stood at my elbow. "Aw, don't let 'em scare you. They used to do me the same way. Now, I got my bluff in on 'em." He drew back an imaginary bean flip and let go.

"I 'spect you do," I mourned, "but they ain't after you."

All afternoon, I worried about what Harold had said. After school, I waited while J.W. retrieved his bean flip. Harold and Sanford hung around, too, with Charlie and Scott Mills. When J.W. and I left the school grounds, the four followed us. J.W. and I speeded up.

"What's the matter, Speer?" Harold called. "Afraid?"

They began running. I took out like a scared rabbit. The boys didn't bother J.W. A quarter-mile ahead, the girls had turned into Virgil McPhetridge's, where we left the road and cut across a field to the Reeder's. In good physical condition from the hard work on the clearing, I out-distanced my pursuer's and turned in the gate. The boys chasing me dropped back.

"We'll get you tomorrow!" Harold shouted.

I slowed, panting. I hoped I wouldn't have to go through this every day.

That night, Papa whipped Opal for not going to school and told her she had to go. The next morning, Opal got ready and left with the rest of us. As soon as she got out of sight of the tent, she ran off and hid in the woods.

The McNutt boys tried to jump me again, that day at school. That night, Papa whipped Opal a second time for not going to school. She beat her fists against her head, cried, and said he could whip her all he wanted to but she still wasn't going to school. He decided he couldn't whip her to death. He walked over to see Virgil Gould on the schoolboard. Mr. Gould agreed it would be all right for Opal to stay home.

Next day, one of the McNutt boys put a small boy up to talking to Hazel, then Harold slipped up and shoved her backwards. She fell, skinning her knee, and cried. I hit Harold with a stick then ran.

After that Harold, Sanford, and some of the other boys picked on us all the time. It became a daily thing that on the way home I had to fight someone. I couldn't whip them and got tired of being beat up. I didn't dare tell Papa. So, we changed our way of going home, cutting through the fields north of the school, then to the Reeders'.

Each day, Mr. Reeder greeted me. "Taw-ig, did you git a whuppin' today in school?"

"No."

"Aw, them dad-gummed teachers, they ain't no good. Can't git a good teacher no more. If I was your teacher, I'd whip you ever'day. If I didn't know what for, you would."

For the most part, we got along well enough in the one-room school. You could hear all the other classes recite. When the eighth graders didn't know the answer to a question, Mr. Watson would ask me. Usually, I knew the answer, especially if it concerned government, for Perry and Papa argued politics all the time.

Hazel spent three days in the second grade, then Mr. Pounds, after hearing her read, put her in the third grade. Another two weeks, he wanted to put her in the fourth grade. Mama sent a note, no, she was too little for the fourth grade.

Papa, Joe, Frank, and Perry finished picking bolls for Mr. Rackley. They picked a few days for Cecil Fairless, George Gould, and Oscar Mercer. Frank ordered new clothes, including a yellow, turtle-necked sweater like Perry's. Mama and Pete's order came, and my new jacket.

One night after supper, Papa started talking about building a cabin in front of the tent. Next day, he and the older boys began marking and cutting down tall pines. Papa built a "lizard" out of the fork of a tree. He hewed the forked end like the runners of a sled. With this, Mike snaked the logs out of the woods and into the clearing. I don't suppose Papa ever considered whose trees those might be. They were on open range and free for the taking as far as he was concerned.

The night before Thanksgiving, Papa took a hankering for a bait of opossum. "Tag, I believe if we'd take old Rex, go down toward the old sawmill on Piney Creek, he might gist tree a 'possum."

This surprised me. "Papa, I don't see how. Rex ain't been trained to 'possum hunt."

"Well, he might as well learn. Let's go."

I got the axe and Papa lit the lantern. The other boys didn't want to go.

"Aw, Rex won't catch anything," Frank said.

Papa and I followed the wagon road leading past Pine Spring and towards Piney. A full moon hung in the sky, making the cold night seem almost bright as day. Rex trotted about smelling the ground, then ran off in the woods. We whooped to him occasionally. He trotted back to us then set off into the woods again.

Papa shifted the lantern. "Well, at least he's a huntin'. He's shore lookin' for one."

Papa could not see too well at night, nor could he walk as fast as I. After about a mile, we heard Rex barking way off in a deep canyon to the north.

"He's a bayin', Papa," I said excitedly.

"Yeah, he has somethin' treed down there. You run on down see what it is. I'll be there soon as I can git there."

I set off in a run. "Git 'em, Rex! Git 'em!"

When I reached Rex, he sat at the foot of a red oak sapling. At the tip of the tree, clung a big opossum.

"Papa, he's got one! Yeah, he's got one! Come on!"

"Yaaa-hooo!" Papa shouted back.

I was afraid the opossum would escape before Papa got there. He soon arrived, grinning and out of breath. "I told you that dog might git one."

"How we goin' to git him down without ruinin' his hide?" I knew a good opossum hide would bring twenty-five to fifty cents.

"Well, you climb up there and shake him out. When he falls, Rex'll grab him; he'll sull up, and play dead."

I skinned up the tree and shook the limb, on which the opossum sat. He clung stubbornly.

"Harder! Possums are hard to shake out."

I shook the limb again. The opossum fell. Rex leaped on him. The opossum sulled. I scrambled from the tree.

Papa called Rex off and picked up the opossum by the back of its neck and cradled him like a football. "You have to be careful how you hold a 'possum. When you carry 'em by the tail, they might look and act dead, but they can bite a plug out of you. So, you keep a firm grip on the back of his neck. That way, he can't wheel around and nail you."

He handed the opossum to me. I held it carefully. I didn't want to repeat the squirrel incident. Rex jumped around us. We started home. Each time the opossum tried to revive, Papa slapped him with a stick, making him sull again.

We circled down by Piney and followed the pipeline to the top of a small canyon and up another ridge. Rex ran into the woods. Half-way home, we heard him bay.

My heart jumped. "He's got somethin' again!"

We located Rex. He had another opossum treed, this one smaller than the first.

Papa craned his neck. "I don't believe you can shake him outa this one. It's too high."

He set down the lantern. We took turns with the axe. When the tree fell, Rex grabbed the opossum. It sulled.

Papa picked it up. "Well, that's purty good for the first night, for a dog that ain't been trained to hunt 'possums."

I anticipated the reactions of the others. "Wait'll we git back to the tent."

I entered the tent alone. Frank looked up. "Well, I see you didn't catch anything."

I bust out grinning. "Come outside and look."

Papa proudly displayed our catch. He put the opossums under a tub, on a large, flat rock. He placed two heavy rocks on top. "If they's any way in the world to git out, a 'possum will find it."

Next morning, Papa took his drawing knife and made two pelt boards, shaped like small ironing boards. He showed us how to kill the opossums without ruining their hides, by laying the axe handle across their necks and pulling on their hindlegs until their necks broke. We gently skinned the opossums so the hide wouldn't tear. Papa turned the hides wrong-side-out, slipped them over the pelt boards, and put them in the little crib so the rats couldn't get them.

"Them pelts ain't good yet," he said. "It takes a good cold spell to make a prime pelt."

At noon, we sat down to a fine thanksgiving dinner of sweet potatoes, baked opossum, and plenty of other vegetables. Papa ate his fill. He liked nothing better than greasy meat. Eating was his vice, but here he could rationalize: "A-body needs to eat a lot to enable him to work a lot."

The next few nights, everyone wanted to go hunting. There weren't many opossum, but sometimes Rex found a trail. Papa advised that we wait until colder weather, when the pelts would be better.

I felt so proud of Rex. Not only was he providing us with meat now, but cash income, too. Besides that, he was a good friend. What more could a boy want in a dog? In addition, we had new clothes, school, plenty to eat, and Papa was building a log cabin.

Life on the clearing continued peaceably, until one cold afternoon in early December, when trouble reared its ugly head once more.

Chapter 16

HOG BUTCHERING

Papa's favorite meat was sausage. When he worked on the WPA, each time he cashed his check, he bought a three-pound carton of sausage at Mr. Cole's meat market in Stuart. This supplemented the free groceries that he obtained from the state commodity truck that came around once a week. Papa could hardly wait until the weather got cold enough for hog butchering.

Recently, Papa had traded two of our pigs and the calf to Leota Ritter's father for a brown jersey cow so we would have more milk. The remaining five pigs weighed about two hundred and fifty pounds each. The first week of December, a cold snap hit.

That afternoon, when the girls and I came home from school, Papa halted in his log hauling. "Tag, you and Joe go find them pigs and drive 'em up. It's gettin' cold enough to butcher."

Joe gazed at him thoughtfully. "Papa, I ain't seen those pigs in a day or two, come to think of it."

"You've been sloppin' 'em at night, ain't you?"

"Yeah, I slopped them last night, but they didn't come up. I don't know where they are."

"Well, they's down there somewhere. You got about an hour 'fore dark. You boys see if you can find 'em.

Drive 'em up here. We'll pen 'em up tonight. Tomorrow, we'll butcher and have fresh meat."

I changed my clothes and called Rex. "Come on, boy! Here, boy! Let's go find them hogs! Git 'em!"

Rex took off. Joe and I followed past the spring and into the woods. We looked and looked for the hogs with Rex scouting in the brush. Occasionally, we called out: "Piggie! Pig, pig, pig!"

We could see where the hogs had been rooting. West of the spring, we heard a noise in the brush. Rex investigated. Out rushed the sow and three pigs.

"Here they are, Joe," I called.

The old sow eyed us balefully.

"Two's missin'," Joe said.

We scouted around. There was no sign of the other pigs.

Joe glanced at the setting sun. "Well, let's chase these on toward home, then go down into Mossy Hollow and look."

"Okay. Come on, Rex, git 'em! Send 'em home!"

With Rex nipping at their heels, the hogs raced up the ridge toward the clearing. Joe and I turned south into Mossy Hollow. After a bit, Rex joined us, his pink tongue hanging out from his exertion.

We searched for the pigs. Dusk came. We pushed on towards Boggy Creek. Near the swinging foot bridge, which crossed the creek near the pipeline, Rex commenced barking. We ran to see what he had found. It was our missing pigs. One was dead and the other half-alive with his ears chewed up and one of his hams about torn off. When he saw us, he squealed and tried to run, but couldn't. It looked as if there had been a terrific scuffle. Paw prints mingled with the pig tracks.

I felt sick, knowing how hard this was going to hit our family's food supply that winter. "What do you reckon happened?"

Joe's fists clenched. "Dogs. Go git Papa. I'll stay here."

I ran over the ridges and through the brush. I burst into the clearing. "Papa! One of the pigs is dead!" I told him what we had found.

Papa's black eyes filled with rage. "I'll be dad-gummed! That son-of-a-bitch! That Lem Hatcher has gone too far. If he's killed my hogs, I'll shoot him!" He ran to the tent and grabbed the old T-Barker shotgun.

Papa, Frank, and I hurried down to where Joe waited.

Grim-faced, Papa studied the tracks and found foot-prints among them. "Yeah, them's Lem Hatcher's tracks. I can tell by his hob-nailed boots."

Papa tightened his grip on the gun, his face a brewing storm. "I'm goin' to lay for him. If I ever find him botherin' anything else of mine, I'm goin' to kill him."

"Now, Papa," Frank said, "you ain't goin' to help your family none. You shoot him and they'll send you to the pen. No use being put away for life over a couple of pigs. We'll git him one of these days. Right now, we better git this other pig home."

Papa sent Joe and me back to the clearing after Mike and the sled. It was dark, when we got back. We hauled the injured hog home. Mama met us with tears in her eyes.

"Henry, that's going to throw us short for winter meat. I was depending on them hogs."

Papa's eyes glittered. "Yeah, that son-of-a-bitch! Ever'time I think about him, I git a little madder. He's takin' the food out of my kids' mouths. I've got a good notion as I've ever had to walk down there right now and blow his guts out!" He broke open the barrel of the shotgun, checked the shell, and snapped it shut. He started back toward Boggy Creek.

Mama wrung her hands. "Henry, no!"

Frank ran after him. "Papa, stop! That won't help. It'll gist make things worse. We got five pigs left.

That'll do for now. We'll git Lem Hatcher, later!"

Papa paused, fury still working in his face. Finally, his anger subsided. "Well, I don't know – " He came back. "I guess we'd better do what we can to save what we got. We'll start butcherin' first thing in the mornin'."

The next day was Saturday. We didn't have a barrel, in which to scald the pigs. Papa had us boys dig a pit down by the horselot between the tent and spring. He built a roaring fire and heated some rocks. He filled the pit with water and added the hot rocks, but couldn't get the water hot enough and the water seeped out.

"Tag, you and Joe, I hate to keep borrowin', but take Mike and the sled. Go over and see if we can use the Reeder's steel barrel."

When we got there, we told the Reeders about our hogs.

Albert's lips pursed. "I've heard plenty about Lem Hatcher. Onct he sic'd his dogs on one of George Williams' hogs like that. I don't know what good he gets outa that. Gist enjoys it. Probably tryin' to run y'all outa there."

Joe looked serious. "Well, I can tell you one thing: Somebody ought to spread the word that Papa's apt to shoot him one of these days if he keeps foolin' around. He was gist about mad enough to do it last night."

"We'll shore tell 'em." Albert promised.

We borrowed their barrel and Mrs. Reeder's iron washpot. Albert and Loren returned with us to help with the hog killing.

Papa, Perry, and Frank had made a platfrom of poles, on which to scrape the hogs. Papa placed the barrel in a hole so the barrel rested at a thirty-five degree angle. We filled the barrel with water and built a fire around it. When the water boiled, Loren shot the pig with his .22.

Papa severed the pig's juglar vein so it would bleed. We hoisted the pig into the scalding water and sloshed it around. We dragged the carcass out on the platform and scraped the bristles with sharp knives, quickly, before the skin cooled. We washed off the pig. Papa cut the leaders of the back legs, stuck a two-foot stick between them, and tied a rope to the stick. We hung the pig in a tree. Papa placed a washtub under the pig and gutted it. Mama and Opal picked the fat off the entrails and saved it for lard.

We killed, cleaned, and gutted the other four hogs. Papa let the meat hang overnight. Sunday morning, we laid the meat on the table in the tent.

"Some things you have to do, Sunday or no," Papa said.

He and Frank cut up the meat, pulling out the ribs, splitting the backbones to make pork chops, and trimming the hams and shoulders for sausage. They had to throw one of the hams from the crippled pig away as it was bruised and bloodshot. Papa salted the middlings and hams with hickory flavored Morton meat packing salt, wrapped them in newspapers, and packed them in orange crates.

"We'll let 'em take salt a week or two," he said, "then hang 'em up to cure."

The loss of the other meat worried Papa. "Tag, you and Betty and Hazel, I know you kids have gist started to school, but tomorrow mornin', I want you to come with us over to Willie Renfro's. He's got a hog about ready to kill. He told me we could have it if we'd pull bolls a couple of days, help him before the ground freezes. So, we'll do that."

I hated to miss school, but the family had to eat. We picked bolls for two days and worked out the hog. He wasn't as fat as ours, but Papa was afraid to turn him out in the woods to fatten up. He butchered him and salted down the meat.

Papa borrowed Reeders' sausage grinder and made sausage, which Mama stuffed into cloth sacks, three pounds to a roll. Perry took three rolls down to Uncle Bryan. Papa sent the Reeders some sausage and ribs.

"I always return favors," Papa said.

When the hams and middlings were ready to remove from the salt, Papa hung each in a tree with a piece of bailing wire to cure. Rex smelled the meat and jumped around beneath it. Papa scolded him and Rex quit.

That night, a loud commotion outside awakened us. Rex barked. Papa jumped out of bed in his long-handles and grabbed his shotgun.

"Somethin's getting the meat!" he said.

We boys jerked on our overalls and shoes and followed. Down by the cribs, a strange dog jumped beneath the meat. He knocked down a middling and began chewing on it.

"G'wan! Git! Beat it!" Papa shouted.

The dog kept on chewing. Papa lifted the gun and let him have it. The dog tumbled end over end, blowed in two. Papa struck a match. We saw it was a big blue dog.

"That's Lem Hatcher's dog," Frank stated flatly.

A chill passed over me. "Papa, you goin' to tell him?"

The match went out. "I ain't goin' to tell him nothin'," Papa spoke grimly. "Gist let him find him."

Before I left for school next morning, Joe and I tied a bailing wire around what was left of the blue dog and dragged him off towards Mossy Hollow. Next day, the buzzards circled there. That evening, Lem Hatcher came sneaking through the woods. Papa had been expecting him and had his shotgun handy.

Hatcher's shifty eyes darted about, taking in everything. "Evening, Mr. Speer. How you folks?"

Papa eyed him coldly. "We'll make it."

Hatcher indicated the pile of logs Papa dragged up. "Looks like y'all fixing to stay awhile. Building a cabin or somethin'?"

"Somethin'." Papa lifted the shotgun a little.

Hatcher glanced at it. "Say, you ain't seen anything of my dog have you? Big blue fella?"

Papa's eyes glittered. "Yeah, I did. I killed him."

Green fire flashed in Hatcher's eyes. "You killed him! What for?"

"For eatin' my meat." Papa patted the shotgun. "I'll kill anything else that threatens my livin'."

The fire in Hatcher's eyes died. "Well, that son-of-a-bitch," he drawled amiably. "Serves his right."

Papa's eyes narrowed. "Somebody sic'd some dogs on a couple of my hogs down on Boggy. I thought maybe they might have been yours."

"Oh, no, it wasn't any of mine, Mr. Speer," Hatcher denied quickly – too quickly. "Fact is, somebody's dogs have been botherin' my hogs, too." He touched his cap. "See you." He melted back into the woods.

Papa's eyes glinted like cold steel. "Look at him go. Looks like a suck-egg dog. He knows gist as well those dogs of his did that. Sneakin' around, tryin' to see what he can find out. I oughta pepper him with the left-hand barrel." Tempted, he lifted the shotgun, thought better of the idea, and lowered the gun. "I'll catch him in the act one of these days. When I do . . ."

His words hung in the air as a troubling promise. In a sense, Papa had already evened things with Lem Hatcher by killing his dog, but Papa didn't like doing this. Even so, that blue dog would have torn down all our meat if Papa had not shot him.

Christmas was fast approaching. We kids didn't expect much. Papa didn't hold with giving a kid many toys. A kid couldn't play with but one at a time, he reasoned. This year we didn't even expect one toy.

At school, our classes were going to draw names and would exchange gifts during a community Christmas program on Christmas Eve. There would be a play and Santa Claus. Papa told Betty, Hazel, and I we couldn't draw names, we didn't have the money to buy presents.

The thought goaded me. I hated to admit we were too poor to exchange gifts. Then, I remembered something. "Papa, how 'bout them two 'possum hides hanging in the crib? Maybe we could sell them?"

He thought a moment. "Yeah, I guess you can do that. They ain't much account though. They won't bring much. You and Joe can catch a ride with the Reeders, and go to town Saturday."

The thought of going to town excited me almost as much as selling the hides and buying the presents. I hadn't been to town since the day we arrived in the community.

On Saturday, J.W. and I rode in the back of the wagon, and Albert, Loren, and Joe in front. Christmas shoppers crowded Stuart. We strolled down the street, staring at the half-dozen cars parked on Main Street and the numerous wagons behind the stores.

The Looney clan, who lived north of Mr. Romine, were drunk and looking for a fight. Lem Hatcher and his family walked down the street. Curley Morris, from C-Bar Prairie, drove by in his green Model-A coupe, headed for McAlester.

We took the opossum hides up to the creamery, where Gene Bernard bought furs and ran the peanut barn. He looked the hides over and gave me thirty cents for the big one and twenty cents for the other.

We walked back to Walter Adams' drugstore. I could smell perfume and candy mingled with that of medicine and leather goods. A candy case and soda fountain stood near the door and opposite, rows of toiletries and medicines.

Walter Adams greeted me with a mouthful of gold teeth shining. "Hello, Speer."

I blinked, puzzled. "How'd you know my name?"

"You all look alike. You Frank Speer's brothers? Henry's boys?"

I nodded.

"I knew it. What do you need?"

I told him I wanted to buy some presents. He showed us his wares. I selected a ten cent comb for Pauline Jones, whose name I had drawn, and Betty and Hazel each a lace-edged handkerchief to take to school. I had two dimes left and gave one to Joe.

Albert and Loren had each bought a Coke and J.W. a M. Hohner harmonica for himself. I thought J.W. was rich. I dallied over the candy case, with its wide array, trying to decide between the peanut squares for a penny each, or the chocolate drops, three for a penny. Then on top of the candy case, I saw a shiny, pink-handled pocketknife for a dime.

I longed to own the knife. I wouldn't have to borrow Papa's any more. I would have my own knife for skinning squirrels, cutting fishing poles, and sharpening sticks to snare rabbits in hollow logs.

"Hey, Joe," I called, "I want you to look at somethin'." I showed him the knife. "I've a notion to spend my dime on this knife. What do you think? What're you going to git?"

He glanced at the sack he held. "I've already spent my dime. I bought Pete a Baby Ruth candy bar and Mama some hair pins for Christmas. I wish we could buy Opal a little something. But, yeah, the knife looks like it'll do to take along."

I wished Joe hadn't said that. I wanted the knife badly, but his words had taken the joy out of it. I put the knife back. I walked to another counter and bought Opal a nickel box of crayons and some smooth paper to draw on.

Christmas Eve, Frank, Perry, and Joe walked with Betty, Hazel, and me over to the school. Opal wouldn't go as usual, though I told her they were handing out candy sacks and had one with her name on it.

At school, Betty had a lead part in the play, Hazel a small part, and I had the role of a black cook. The audience clapped and whistled at the end. Willie Renfro played Santa Claus and handed out the presents. Each time he called out a name, I expected it to be mine. Finally, the presents were all gone and I didn't get one. Hurt welled up in my throat. Whoever had my name hadn't bought me one.

"Why don't you tell Charley Watson," Perry suggested.

"I'd rather do without," I choked.

We each received a candy sack and two more for Pete and Opal. I found an orange, some nuts, and hard candy in mine. That eased some of my disappointment.

Back home, Frank had cut a small cedar tree. Opal decorated the tree with strings of popcorn and red buck berries during our absence. We ate our candy and nuts with Christmas cheer. After everyone went to bed, Joe and I placed our presents for Mama, Pete, and Opal beneath the tree. Next morning, that's all there were.

Mama's eyes filled with tears. "I guess Santa Claus couldn't find us down here in the clearin'."

She slid a ham into the wood stove and scurried about making pies. She had not heard from any of the older kids in Tulsa, but hoped some of them might come down. About 11:30 a.m., a yellow cab pulled into the clearing.

"It's Albert and Drucy!" Hazel hollered.

They were loaded down with presents and groceries, Drucy fat and jolly, Albert tall and thin. Scarcely had we sat down to dinner, when another car drove into the clearing and honked. I looked out of the tent. It was Bud and Eunice's green Studebaker. They'd been stuck on the clay hill over by Sam Blassingame's. They brought more groceries and presents.

I strutted around in my gift from Albert and Drucy, a yellow Boy Scout bandana with a pencil clasp. Bud and Eunice gave me a pair of leather boots with the price tag still attached: $1.29. In a little pocket on one of the boots, I found a pocketknife with two blades. My eyes got all silly and watered up.

Betty and Hazel received some underwear; Opal perfume and a manicure set; Pete a truck; Joe some Rose Hair Oil and socks; Papa a flannel shirt and smoking tobacco; Mama a sweater and a pair of dime-store eye glasses. Perry and Frank each got a can of Shinola shoe polish and a pack of Camels.

Frank stuck his Camels in his pocket. "I'm going to keep mine until I go to preachin'."

"You do and the Reeders'll bum you out of them," Perry said.

"That's a'right," Frank said. "I've bummed plenty of smokes off them."

Neither Albert and Drucy nor Eunice and Bud had any kids and they loved them. Bud, a small man with big ears, who was an avid hunter and fisherman, handed Pete a new pair of striped coveralls.

Pete's face lit. "B-Bud, did you g-git these off the welfare like T-Tag did?"

Bud squatted beside Pete. "No, I got these from Santa Claus. I met him about daylight over by Calvin. Just as we drove off that bridge, there by that chug-hole, I spotted him down by the willow, watering his reindeers. I guess they were thirsty after flying all night."

Pete's eyes bugged.

"Well, sir," Bud went on, "a green-headed mallard lit on the horns of one of them deer. I grabbed my .410 and leveled down on that duck. Santa Claus said, 'Oh, no! Stop, you might scare my reindeer!' Then he asked me, 'Say, do you know Pete Speer? He lives in a tent over west of Reeders. A little tousle-headed boy."

Albert winked at the rest of us. "One that likes to goose mules?"

Bud nodded in agreement. "One that likes to goose mules. 'He's my brother,' I told Santa Claus. 'I'm just fixing to go over there.' 'Well, then would you take these coveralls to him? Tell him I started over there, but one of my reindeers threw a shoe, and I had to hurry on back to the North Pole.' I said I would. So, here's your Christmas present, Pete." He held out a new pair of coveralls.

Pete, who had been listening to Bud's story in open-mouthed wonder, clutched the coveralls to his chest.

We sat down to eat again, an excellent meal. The laughter rose and fell with the conversation. After dinner, Albert took a nap, Bud went hunting with Rex, and Papa, Eunice, and Perry argued politics.

Late in the afternoon, when the company mentioned going home, Opal began begging to go with them.

Papa's brow lifted. "Why, Opal, what would you do up there?"

"Stay with Avis and Charley. Avis said I could."

Papa glanced at Eunice. She nodded in confirmation.

"Well, I guess you can then. They's not much to do here right now and we're all cooped up. Come spring, you have to come home. I'll need you then.

I don't think Opal heard this last. She was already getting her clothes.

Frank had been studying Bud and Albert. Each day, he had grown more discontent. He was in love with Leota Ritter and wanted to get married and set up, but he didn't see how, on the clearing.

"How 'bout me goin', too, up to Tulsa and try to git on?" he said.

Silence fell.

"Well, jobs are scarce," Albert warned.

Papa frowned. "Son, you're better off to stay with the land."

Bud nodded in agreement. "Winter's a bad time to be out in the world without nothin', Frank."

"Anytime's a bad time to be without nothin'." Frank rose. "I believe I'll gist do her."

Chapter 17

LONG WINTER EVENINGS

Life seemed lonesome on the clearing without Frank and Opal, but the work went on as usual.

Papa, Joe, and Perry laid up the logs for the cabin. They sawed some red oaks into two-foot cuts. Mr. Reeder came over and split the cuts into shake shingles in exchange for the scrap wood for his hungry fireplace.

Mama's household chores had increased without Opal's help, but peace reigned in the tent. Pete played with his new truck. Betty, Hazel, and I became more involved with our schooling and social activities.

I suppose the biggest adjustment anyone has to make, when moving to a new community is the social change. This is especially true when moving from the city to the backwoods as we did.

Frank had no trouble fitting in, even in the beginning. He had lived here before. His good looks made him popular with the young people. The community looked down on the rest of us though, because of our financial circumstances.

Eventually, our school grades helped Betty, Hazel, and me somewhat in establishing ourselves. That winter, we took part in school plays and social events at the church. The community held a number of these on cold winter nights, when there wasn't much else to do.

Saturday nights, the young people usually gathered at the church-house for singing. We attended play parties at someone's home. Perry, Joe, and I might run three or four miles after dark to a neighbor's home to play "forty-two," or go over to Reeders' to visit and listen to the Victrola.

Sometimes, we participated in kangaroo court at the church. This involved a mock trial on trumped up charges – the more ludicrous, the funnier. The first one I attended was on New Year's Eve. Haskell Lane sued Cleburn Pounds over alienation of Willie Crosswaite's affection. I listened closely to the "lawyers." Being a natural-born ham, I decided next time I could be the lawyer.

I knew a lot of legal terms like "corpus delicti," which I had picked up from *Dick Tracy* in the funny papers. I dug out a gray, pin-stripped vest, which Bud had sent down once. When my turn came at the church, I walked back and forth before the audience, thumbs hooked in my vest, presenting my case in a convincing manner.

Afterward, Buster Jones, a farmer noted for his singing ability, slapped his knee. "By dog, if I ever get in trouble, I believe I'd druther have Tag defend me than any of them lawyers over at McAlester. I believe he could out-talk 'em."

These social events gave us young people a chance to meet and have fun together. There was little pairing off between the boys and girls. Most of the boys I knew respected the girls. Dancing was forbidden for usually drinking and fighting went with it. So, only the rougher citizens danced.

Returning home at night, we walked in a group, laughing and talking. Way off through the woods, we could see old lady Griffin's lamp shining in her window, on a hill near Rock Creek. The stars seemed close enough to touch and the world lay at peace.

Other evenings, we read a lot. I read the Bible

through twice that winter. Within four months, I had read everything the school's small library contained.

Papa liked to read my library books, too. He especially liked *Robinson Crusoe*, because, while on that island, Robinson Crusoe came to know the Lord.

Sometimes, Papa asked what I had learned in school that day. Once, I told him that before many years, instead of people just talking through the air like radio, we'd have a thing called television, which would send pictures, too.

Papa snorted like a mule. "Son, that's a bunch of tom foolery. Even if they do, they'll be so many trees and fence posts in the picture, a-body can't tell what he's a lookin' at. It gists stands to reason. Next thing you know, somebody'll git the notion he can fly to the moon."

At school, I hung on every word Mr. Watson said about men like Kit Carson and Daniel Boone. In class, I was the only one who knew that the forking off place for those bound for California on the Oregon Trail was Fort Hall, Idaho. I'd read *The Oregon Trail* by Francis Parkman.

Grammar was something else. I never could get it through my head how an adjective was the name of a person, place, or thing, and how a noun described something. Mama and Papa were both of pioneer stock from Tennessee and Alabama. They used a lot of mountaineer expressions. When Papa wanted to name or describe something, he just up and done it without bothering with all that grammar stuff. I talked a lot like Papa and Mama.

Each week, we got the funny papers. Pete went from one to the other of us kids to read them to him. Then Pete "read" them back to us.

Papa said, "Why look at that boy. I believe that boy can read!" Of course he couldn't. Pete had the words memorized by then.

Sometimes, in the evenings, Hazel combed Papa's

hair, which she liked to do. In his fine tenor voice, Papa sang songs, such as *"The Preacher and the Bear."* Mama rocked Pete and sang to him such songs as, *"Ratty Bow, Rink To My Climbo"; "Poor Little Kitty Cat, Poor Little Feller"*; or *"Big Tom, Little Tom, Big Tom Bailey."* We played checkers with a homemade set sawed from a tree limb, which we colored with crayons.

Most of all, on a long winter evening, when the snow blew outside the tent, we liked to gather around the heating stove, eat popcorn and peanuts, and beg Papa for a story about Scott County, Arkansas.

Papa would fill his corncob pipe, lean back in his chair, and close his eyes. Sometimes, he told us about when he was a boy, with Grandpa and the rest of his family living in a cabin on Mill Creek; or about the witch who lived near them and how she hexed their cow. Grandpa threatened to shoot the witch with a silver bullet. Next day, their cow got well.

Papa related his parents' beliefs. They thought that tomatoes were poison. So were tarantulas, praying mantis, or "horse devils." If an orange and blue centipede crawled on you, your flesh would rot. If you killed a snake and left it laying on its back, it would not die until sundown. If a turtle bit you, he would not turn loose until it thundered. If you picked up a toad you got warts. A gypsy could take the warts off by hiding a dishrag. People believed a madstone would cure rabies. You got a madstone from the stomach of a solid white cow or deer. You soaked the madstone in sweet milk and it would stick to a sure enough mad dog bite and draw out all the poison.

Sometimes, Papa told us about our grandparents, Samuel Speer and Lydia Jane Melton, or our great-grandfather, Moses Martin Speer, who owned eleven slaves before the Civil War.

"Liddy's" family had lived near Chattanooga, Tennessee, when the Civil War broke out. The men went off to fight for the South, leaving the women and girls to tend the crops. The women ground parched okra seeds for coffee and boiled the dirt from the smokehouse to obtain salt.

After the war, Samuel and Liddy married. Samuel and his brothers, Jess, John, and Will, decided to move west. On horseback, they scouted the land through Tennessee, Arkansas, and Indian Territory. After three months, they selected land in Sebastian County, Arkansas. They moved in a group, the four brothers, sister Fanny, Moses Martin Speer, and their families.

Sometimes, on these long winter nights, as Papa talked, someone was sure to beg, "Papa, tell us a bear tale."

"Bears don't have any tail," Papa wisecracked.

"Tell us 'bout Old Loud," I would urge. "I like to hear 'bout Grandpa's dog."

Papa squinched his eyes. "Oh, pshaw, I've told you young uns that yarn a hundred times."

"I know, Papa, but I never git tired of hearin' it. How'd you git that old dog?"

Papa punched up the fire a little, refilled his pipe, leaned back, and began talking.

He told us about the time he, Grandpa, and Fanny drove to Waldron in the ox wagon to get some corn ground. A big hound with fine, blue hair like a mole, followed them home. They learned later he was a Plotts hound. The kids called him Old Loud. They took him hunting. Old Loud would hunt anything they wanted him to, including grasshoppers for fish bait.

Once, a bear got into the corn patch. Grandpa and Uncle Jess put Old Loud on the trail. They lost him. That evening, they heard him come back around the mountain, still after something. They went with their guns and found Old Loud had a bear backed into a bend in the rocks. Old Loud was all ripped open, his lip and one of his ears torn about half off. Grandpa shot the bear and brought it home.

The reputation of Old Loud grew up and down Mill Creek, as being the best all-around dog around there. One day, when Grandpa, Uncle Jess, and Papa went to Waldron to do some trading, they saw a guy there with a pet bear tied with a log chain.

Someone said, "Sam, you think your dog is so good, I'll bet he wouldn't fight old Clyde's bear."

Grandpa said, "I don't bet; I'm a preacher. But he'd fight him if I put him onto him."

Everyone went to hooting and hollering. They said there wasn't a dog in Waldron that would go near that bear. Grandpa said Old Loud would. Finally, he told them if Clyde would put a muzzle on the bear so he couldn't hurt Old Loud, he would show them.

They went up to a stockade corral and Clyde muzzled the bear. Papa sic'd Old Loud onto the bear. The bear slammed Old Loud on the side of the head and rolled him over about ten feet. Old Loud darted back in. The bear caught him across the top of the head and ripped his hide loose. Old Loud circled the bear, snapping and grabbing at him. The bear stood on his hindlegs and slapped at Old Loud. Old Loud jumped back, then grabbed the bear's throat and wouldn't turn loose. The bear couldn't get him off. Finally, Clyde begged Grandpa to call Old Loud off before he killed the bear.

Stories like this filled me with contentment as I listened. I felt proud of Grandpa and Old Loud and glad I had Rex.

The log cabin walls grew higher with the passing of winter. Papa, Perry, and Joe chinked the walls with clay. They built the roof and made a door and windows. The middle of February, a year after we moved to the clearing, we moved into the cabin. It felt good having solid walls around us again and all that room. We put our beds in the cabin, and Mama kept the tent for a kitchen.

Sometimes, I wondered about Frank and Opal up at Tulsa. One day, when I looked up, I saw Frank coming across the clearing. Frank gazed at the cabin in surprise.

Papa welcomed him. "I'd be pleased to know what you been doin'? Did you find work?"

Frank shook his head. "I did see a sign in one store that said, 'Come on inside out of the Depression,' but I couldn't find work. I helped Virgil Gray in his upholstery shop some. He 'marked it down,' but that was all. I'm broke as when I left."

A grieved look crossed Papa's seamed face. "I'm sorry you had to find it out the hard way. The city's a bad place to be durin' the Depression, but the land, she's steady."

I was content with the clearing, especially now that Frank was back. We had the beginning of a real home. We were squeezing our food, but planting time lay around the corner. I thought we could last out the Depression comfortably enough. With spring, though, new trouble reared its ugly head.

Chapter 18

SPRING AGAIN

Maybe we had cabin fever, or maybe it was the constant pressure for survival on the clearing. Anyway, by spring, it seemed everyone's temper was short.

Frank had come back from Tulsa disillusioned and heartsick. He saw no way of cutting loose from the family and setting up on his own.

The WPA had started a bridge project on Boggy Creek, near Oscar Mercer's place. Papa worked there two days a week, but as usual, he could not get along with the other men. He preached the Bible and praised the New Deal on the job and on the streets of Stuart.

"You people stand around and cuss the government," he said. "I don't blame Hoover for the Depression. I blame him 'cause he didn't do nothin'. If we let the government control the plantin' and stop over-plantin', prices will go up. The economy is like our blood supply. If you cut off the blood supply, the body dies. If you cut off the money supply, the economy dies. That's what Roosevelt's tryin' to do – tryin' to git the money back in the hands of the little people – tryin' to keep it circulatin'!"

Papa couldn't talk about anything else. It embarrassed the rest of us and caused turmoil on his job.

"What we ought to do is go down there and whip that old man," P.R. Davis said one day, when in town.

Hoyt Ritter, Leota's brother, said, "P.R., I don't believe you and them others can whip Mr. Speer and me."

Nevertheless, some of the men talked of going to Holdenville to see if they could get Papa laid off work. Hoyt got word to Papa. Papa sent Frank to work in his stead for the duration of the bridge project.

Ever since he had blood poisoning, carbuncles had plagued Frank on his arms and legs. The risings throbbed as he dug rock and clay to put on the road. All he earned went to Papa to support the family.

Papa got Frank a few more days work for Carrol Greenhall in exchange for seed corn. Frank walked the six miles down there and back each day.

When March came, Papa set Joe to plowing with the mule and rest of us to clearing more new ground. Frank said nothing to Papa, but it hurt him that Joe got to plow instead of him as the eldest.

Papa and Perry couldn't get along for any length of time. Perry bossed the rest of us kids and teased Pete. Hard of hearing, he often thought we were faulting him or making fun of him. He resented being corrected, when he mispronounced a word. At meeting, he scolded me and told me not to talk so much, telling everyone our business. He came down with malaria. As spring advanced, Perry became more outspoken about the clearing and its deprivation.

"Hughes County is the poorest county per capita in Oklahoma," he argued with Papa. "Ever'body here will always struggle for a livin'. If you aim to farm, why don't you go some place where you can make money?"

"I got nowhere to go and no way to git there," Papa said.

I grew tired of Perry's arguing. "If you don't like livin' here, why don't you take off?"

"I'm aimin' to. I'm thinkin' about it," he said.

Word came that Mr. Rackley and all his family were down with the fever and very ill. Papa sent Joe, Frank, and Perry over there to plow and help with the planting.

"That's what good neighbors are for," Papa said.

Papa got the idea of planting a big patch of potatoes for a cash crop. The middle of March, Charley McClure and Avis camed down and brought two hundred pounds of seed potatoes. Opal came home with them.

Right off, I could see Opal didn't want to come back. She acted resentful and scarcely spoke to anyone. Pete tried to hug her, and she brushed him away. When she discovered Betty had taken over her drawer in the bottom of the wardrobe, Opal threw her things out, crumpling her papers.

"Mama! Look what Opal's doing to my stuff!" Betty cried.

Opal glared, openly hostile.

Avis, an attractive woman with dark hair and eyes, spoke in a low tone, "Mama, I don't know about Opal. She don't seem like herself any more. All she does is sit around and look moody. We couldn't get her to do anything, go anywhere."

Mama frowned. "Don't look like she'd been that way. Tulsa is where she wanted to go so bad."

"Mama, I think something's wrong with her. I don't think her internal organs are developing right. She's old enough to start her womanhood – " Avis paused on the brink of a delicate subject.

Mama fingered a crease in her apron. "I know. All that hard work Opal did in the fields alongside the boys, I was afraid it might hurt her. Henry didn't like it either, but seems like he had to have her."

Avis shook her head. "Well, I don't know whether that done it or not, but something's wrong with her."

During the next few days, I could see Avis was right. Opal would be outside the tent, talking to herself. Not that I considered that so strange. When in the woods alone, I'd talk to myself sometimes. However, Opal talked to herself, answered, and laughed, even when others were around.

That weekend, Albert and Loren Reeder came down. Opal ran to the woods and stayed hidden half a day. Mama called and called her.

When Opal finally came back, Mama said, "Where you been?"

"Oh, gist out there," Opal said.

"What were you doin'?"

"Gist thinkin'."

Opal became very secretive and didn't want to do her chores. Papa didn't know whether she was just being stubborn or what.

Perry said, "If I was Papa, I'd make her do it. She's only bein' mule-headed."

Perry teased Opal and called her Snuffy. Papa got onto him and they argued about Opal.

Papa found Perry a few days work breaking land for Arch Ruble in exchange for sorghum seed. Arch lived south of Buford McNutt.

One Sunday afternoon, as Perry walked home from visiting Uncle Bryan, he heard a commotion at the top of Hickerson Hill. Looking up, he saw Buford's team – a white mule and a black horse – careening over the hill. In the wagon, clung Maude McNutt, Sanford, and Odell. They were on their way to Buster Jones' for the singing. Maude sawed desperately on the reins, screaming, "Whoa! Whoa!"

It was a runaway! Perry stood rooted a moment. He jumped into the middle of the road. As the team swept past, he grabbed a bridle in each hand and dug in his heels. "Whoa! Whoa!"

He lost his footing. The team dragged him about thirty feet. Maude screamed. Perry twisted around, and finally managed to regain his footing. He jerked on the bridles and dug his heels in again. "Whoa!"

At last, the team stopped and stood trembling in the road. Maude broke into tears of relief.

The following day, news of Perry's heroic rescue spread over the community. Buford McNutt's attitude toward Papa changed immediately. He became a true friend. He always had a kind regard for Perry after that.

While Perry's heroism helped smooth community relations, it only seemed to make Perry more bossy on the clearing, or so I thought.

One afternoon, Perry and I were sawing wood while Betty sat on the log to keep it from rolling. I was already angry with Perry for always being so critical. It seemed everything I had done that day had been wrong in Perry's viewpoint.

"Quit bearin' down so hard on your end of the saw," Perry complained.

"Aw, go to hell," I mumbled, taking advantage of his hard of hearing handicap.

Perry paused in suspicion. "What did you say?"

"I said, 'Okay, I'll do it,'" I lied.

We commenced sawing again. I glanced at Perry and mumbled meaningless words.

Perry paused again. "What?"

"I didn't say anything."

His face turned red. "I know damn well you did. Quit doin' me that way!"

I pulled the trick on him again. Perry dropped the saw handle, jumped over the log, and nabbed me. We rolled across the ground, pounding, and gouging.

Betty screamed and flew towards the cabin. "Papa! Papa!"

Papa was there in seconds. Perry was bigger than I. About all I could do was protect myself from his pounding fists. Papa dragged him off, Perry still fighting to get to me.

"Hold it, Newt!" Papa ordered. "What in the Sam Hill

is the matter with you John Brown young uns? I try to raise you like decent folks, and you have to act like heathens. Always rough-housin' and fightin'!"

"Make him shut his mouth!" Perry said. "He's always makin' fun of me, and tryin' to pull things on me!"

"Well, if you'd quit tryin' to boss him and leave the raisin' of these young uns to me, maybe you wouldn't have so much trouble around here," Papa said.

Perry bristled. "Old man, if that's the way you feel about it, you can have my part of it! Anybody that'd sit around here and work their guts out on land that ain't theirs is foolish anyway. You're only fixin' it up for somebody else to git."

Papa raised his hand. "Don't call me foolish. The Bible says a man who don't rule his own house is worse than an infidel."

"Aw, cripe with that stuff," Perry grumbled. "I'm gittin' out of here. I'm goin' to California – some place where a person can make a decent livin' at somethin' more than fifty cents a day."

He marched towards the cabin. Guilt crawled through me, for starting the ruckus. Soon, Perry came out with his cardboard suitcase, his clothes crammed into it.

Mama stood in the doorway, face drawn in anxiety. "Perry, can't you wait until tomorrow? At least until after supper?"

"Aw, ain't no use hangin' around here. I been ready to take off for some time anyway."

He limped from the clearing, his suitcase banging against his bad leg.

I felt awful. I went to Mama, trying to soothe her worry. "He'll be a'right, Mama."

Tears filled her gray eyes, and she couldn't speak.

Opal followed Perry as far as the gate. She stood staring down the road a long time after he vanished from sight.

In the days that followed, the spring planting continued. Joe guided Mike across the land, throwing up ridges and turning them under. We bent, stooped, and hoed. We chopped and dug out more new ground. Our burning brush piles sent black smoke into the sky. Sometimes, when I paused to get a drink from the water jug, half-buried in the ground to keep it cool, I thought about what Perry had said about the land.

"Frank," I said one day, "who do you reckon owns this land?"

"No tellin', but I know who'd shore like to have it."

"Yeah, Lem Hatcher." I glanced around the clearing. The crops were up and the new cabin stood before the tent. "I expect the more we do here, the more he'd like to have it. You know, it'd git to me if I figgered we was doin' all this work gist so somebody like him could git it."

"Ain't that the truth, oh, by dolly."

The work was easier with the mule, I had to admit. Mama, Betty, and Hazel, picked wild greens down by the old sawmill. Rex lazed in the sun, treed squirrels, and helped me bring up Roady for the evening milking.

Late in April, Papa had Roady bred over at Buford McNutt's. Buford refused to charge him for it. Frank and I led the sow – rather she led us – over to Virgil Gould's and had her bred, too. That spring promised to be the beginning of another bumper crop year, but tragedy never seemed far from the clearing.

Things began innocently enough. When we were planting the garden, little Pete was always "planting" something, too, perhaps his marbles, a rusty pocket knife, or something like that.

Pete always had to eat with a spoon with a bent handle. Pete hated that spoon. One day, late in May, Pete saw the spoon laying beside his dinner plate. He slipped the spoon outside and buried it behind the tent.

Opal saw what Pete was doing. She dug up the spoon,

took it back inside the tent, and showed it to Pete. "See what I got!" she taunted.

"G-Gimme that spoon!" Pete squalled. "I'll bury it again!" He snatched the spoon and ran back outside.

Opal followed. At the edge of the cabin, she tripped over a tent rope and fell, striking the back of her neck, on one of the tent stakes. She screamed in pain.

We all dropped our work and ran to her. Opal writhed on the ground.

Mama paled. "Get her inside."

Frank and Joe carried Opal into the cabin and laid her on a bed. Opal cried in agony and clutched her neck. The point of impact was red and beginning to swell. Mama bathed the injury in cold water. Shortly, Opal fell asleep.

Mama frowned. "That's not a good sign."

Papa dismissed it, trying not to worry. "Aw, she'll be a'right, Larrie. She's gist tired and run down."

The next couple of days, all Opal wanted to do was sleep. Mama fussed and worried over her. She rubbed Opal's neck. When Opal tried to turn her head, she cried out in pain. In about three days, the swelling went down and Opal seemingly began to recover.

"Oh, I guess she'll be all right," Mama said.

From that time on, though, Opal began acting even stranger. When she returned to work, we had to watch her all the time. Sometimes, she stopped in the middle of something and began cryin'; or she ran into the woods and hid, and someone had to go find her. There was a strangeness about her we couldn't understand.

Decoration Day came. We kids went to "dinner on the grounds" at Bohannon Church. The community always observed the holiday on the Sunday before that date, and the churches of the area took turns sponsoring it. People came in cars, wagons, on horseback, and on foot.

In the morning, we held a preaching service and

singing in honor of the dead. At noon, everyone spread his picnic lunch and ate. After this, all got out their homemade flowers, and met at the cemetery gate. Tooley Green led in prayer. Mr. Reeder, the oldest person present, led the procession through the cemetery to decorate the graves while everyone sang, *"Yes, we shall gather at the river . . ."*

Loren Reeder stood around wearing a pair of dime-store glasses he had received in a trade with Perry. "Do I look any different since I got my glasses?" he asked.

June came warm and sunny. We spent endless days working the crops, burning stumps, fence building, carrying water, and chopping wood.

One thing we kids had learned early on the clearing was never to say we didn't have anything to do. Papa could always fill that void in a hurry. He believed the best way to keep a "young un" happy, free from boredom, and out of mischief was to keep him busy.

He sure tried to practice what he advocated.

Sometimes, he left us kids to work alone, not that he was lazy himself, but he had a lot on his mind keeping everything else going.

More often, he worked beside us, stripped to his B.V.D. top. The joy of the land seemed to fill his being. He would sing: *"On that bright and cloudless morning, when the dead in Christ shall rise . . . ."*

We kids dragged to the cabin at night, dead tired. Even Mike tried to go to the house, when he could. I longed for the weekends when we could rest.

One fine Saturday, about noon, we were all lined out, hoeing and thinning the corn, when Rex barked. We looked up to see Albert, Loren, and J.W. walking through the gate. Each had a rolled-up pack on his back, and their little feist trotted beside them.

"Let's go fishing!" Albert called.

My heart leaped. Opal sped to the woods.

Frank glanced at Papa. "What do you think? We're

'bout done here. Do we have to work this afternoon?"

Papa eyed the remaining work. "Well, I'll tell you, Albert, you boys chip in and help, and it'll only take a short while to git through. Then I'll let ever'body off to go fishin'."

Everyone whooped. The Reeders dropped their packs and grabbed a hoe. In no time, we had that corn finished.

Frank, Joe, and I hustled to the house to get our fishing hooks and something for dinner and supper.

"No need to take a skillet," Loren said. "We got all that stuff and some eggs. We're goin' to kill a squirrel, and we'll have fish."

In a few minutes, we were ready, each of us with a rolled-up backpack.

Frank carried a lantern. "Papa, we're goin' to spend the night. Be back tomorrow."

Papa nodded. "We'll have the fryin' pan ready."

We set off, southeast towards the pipeline, all excited and laughing. Rex trotted beside the feist.

I glanced at J.W. "Where're we going?"

"Over on Boggy. There's a deep hole there."

My skin crawled. "Up by Lem Hatcher's?"

"Yeah, anti-gogglin', 'bout a mile from there."

"You think we oughta?"

J.W. caught my meaning. "We've fished there before. Lem Hatcher ain't never bothered us."

Frank hesitated. "Yeah, but Papa kinda likes us to stay away from his land – ever since the hog and dog killings."

Albert squinted. "We ain't goin' to be on his land, at least not for long. Just cross it a little ways to git to the creek."

"Lem Hatcher comes around your land all the time," Loren argued. "You don't bother him. 'Sides, we want go there. There's a deep hole for swimmin'."

Joe grinned. "I'll buy that!"

It sounded good to me, too. "Come on then, let's go!"

We crossed Mossy Hollow into the Boggy bottoms. We came upon a working sawmill in Will Orr's pasture. The saw, driven by an old truck engine, whined as we approached. A young man snaked up big cottonwood logs with a team of oxen. An older man pushed logs into the blade, while a tow-headed boy jumped into the sawdust and did his best to cut off his fingers in the saw.

The old man idled the saw. His face looked aged as a piece of old leather with shoe-button black eyes and a handle-bar mustache. He wore a sweat-stained shirt, blue overalls, and a greasy cap. "How ye boys doin'?"

"Fine as frog's hair split three ways," Albert said. "You gittin' many big logs in here?"

The old man got a drink and spat the warm water on the grôund. "Not many. The sons-a-bitches are too hard to drag in and outa here."

The little boy, shoeless, with ragged overalls, a snotty nose, and hair that looked as if it had never seen a comb, glanced up at the swear word. "Pam-paw, Pam-paw – "

"What, man?" the old man answered in a patient voice, without glancing at the boy.

"The old booger man's gonna git you."

"I know it, man. Where you boys goin' fishin'?"

"Down on Boggy below Lem Hatcher's," Loren said.

"Better be careful, don't find any stills hidden there. I don't know if you can catch any damn fish in there or not."

"Pam-paw, Pam-paw," the boy insisted again.

"What, man?"

"The old booger man's gonna git you."

"I know it, man."

"Well, we're goin' to give it a whirl," Albert said.

"If'n I didn't have to run this son-of-a-bitchin' mill all the time, I'd go with ye."

"Pam-paw, Pam-paw – "

"What, man?"

"The old booger man's gonna git you."

"I don't give a damn, man," the old man said kindly.

"Well, Pam-paw, if you don't care, I don't give a damn either," the boy replied solemnly, and returned to his playing.

We left, still laughing.

We followed Boggy upstream to the bridge, about a half-mile south of Hatcher's house. We crossed the bridge, went through Hatcher's pasture gate, up a trail about fifty yards, and into George Williams' pasture. Half-a-mile beyond, we came to the fishing hole.

We set out a dozen hooks, then went upstream to the swimming hole. We stayed in the water about an hour, then checked our hooks. Frank, Joe, Loren, and Albert went off up the creek, squirrel hunting with the dogs. J.W. and I cut bamboo poles and fished for perch. We hunted around for bullfrogs. In about an hour, the others returned with a squirrel. J.W. and I had eight goggle-eyed perch and three yellow catfish.

We went swimming again. About sundown, we dragged up dead limbs and built a fire. Loren and Frank cooked the squirrel and fish. We ate and lounged on our quilts. The others smoked and the dogs rested beside us.

"This is the most damn fun I've had in a long time," Loren declared.

I grinned. "Pam-paw, Pam-paw – "

"What, man?" Loren replied.

"That old booger man's gonna getcha."

"I don't give a damn!"

We rolled on our quilts, laughing.

We sat up most of the night, running our fishing lines, playing cards beside the fire, laughing, and telling ghost stories. Loren played his harmonica and J.W. his jew's-harp. Albert and Frank sang, "*Rosewood Casket*."

We fished until next morning about ten. We swam again till noon. By then, we were tired and ready to go home. I called Rex. He had run off up the creek. We could hear him, about a mile off, baying.

"He's got somethin' treed," I said. "Should we go to him?"

The other boys felt too tired and sleepy to go.

Frank said, "Aw, gist call him in."

We called and called. Rex wouldn't come. This worried me.

Frank gathered his stuff. "Aw, he'll be a'right. He'll come in, when it gits dark. Let's go."

We left Rex on Boggy and went home. Rex didn't come in that evening, nor was he home the next morning.

Deep lines creased Papa's face. "Where is he?"

"We left him treed," Frank said. "We thought he'd come on in."

Papa waited an hour or two longer. "Somethin's wrong with that dog. He'd of been here by now. I'm goin' down there and see if I can call him."

He left the clearing, moving down the ridge towards Boggy. Although the sun was hot, a chill crossed my arms.

Chapter 19

EVICTED

Papa walked way off down the ridge. He called and called Rex, his voice floating back to us in the clearing. Rex didn't come. Papa returned.

"Frank, you and Joe better go see about him. He might be caught in somethin', or somebody might have got him." An ominous undercurrent rang in his tone.

Frank and Joe disappeared in the direction of Boggy Creek, walking fast. All kinds of thoughts flashed through my mind. I wished we had gone after the dog. I wished we had never gone fishing and swimming down by Lem Hatcher's. I remembered March and I didn't know if I could bear to lose another dog.

Late that afternoon, Frank and Joe swung back up the trail. Rex was not with them.

"We found him," Frank began without preamble. "He's dead."

Shock rippled through me. For a moment, I felt as if I was going to faint.

"We walked all around," Joe said in a thick voice. "He was laying in the creek -- castrated!" He broke off, unable to continue.

"The wound had got infected," Frank continued. "Rex was tryin' to git to water. His tongue --the flies --" His voice broke, his throat working.

Hot tears stung my eyes. My throat ached and I could scarcely breathe.

"We figger Lem Hatcher done it," Frank concluded, "gist like George Williams' bull. Gist full of meaness."

I couldn't bear any more. I burst into loud sobs that tore at my throat. Betty, Hazel, and Pete cried too. Papa's face tightened into a steel mask. He stepped into the cabin and returned with the old T-Barker shotgun. He broke open the breech and thumbed a green shell into each barrel. He strode down the ridge towards Boggy Creek.

Mama ran after him, her face lined with fear. "Henry!"

Frank followed. "Papa, it won't do any good! You don't have any proof it was Hatcher!"

Papa kept going, his legs covering the ground in long strides. "That dog is proof enough. I've stood all I'm goin' to from that son-of-a-bitch. The rest of you stay here. I'm goin' alone."

He disappeared among the trees. Mama and Frank came back slowly, tears sliding down Mama's care-worn cheeks.

Unable to bear it all, I ran to the woods and flung myself down beneath a hickory tree. Uncontrollable sobs wracked my shoulders. I cried until I could cry no more. Dusk came. Off in the woods, a whipporwill called, and a mourning dove sounded its plaintive call. I dared not think of the future, and listened for the sound of a distant gunshot. It did not come, and I returned to the clearing, feeling numb inside.

Moving woodenly, Mama set supper on the table beneath the brush arbor. Nobody felt like eating. Papa's chair at the head of the table stood empty, like a menacing specter. Mama lit the lantern. Ghostly shadows flickered about us. At last, we heard footsteps crunching up the path leading from the spring. Papa stepped into the light, and leaned the shotgun against a post. His drawn face looked weary and gray. I held my breath, fearing the worst.

Papa shook his head in answer to our unspoken question. "I couldn't do it. I had the son-of-a-bitch in my sights and I couldn't do it. All I could think of was, '*Thou shalt not kill.*'"

Mama sank into a chair and broke into muffled sobs of relief. I began to breathe again.

Papa sat down heavily on the bench beside the table and pulled off his shoes. "He may have seen me. I don't know. Don't matter much. We're even now on the dogs. We can git another dog. From here on, if he will leave us alone, we'll leave him alone. You can make peace with the birds and animals, but you can't with people. Some of them are gist a natural-born son-of-a-bitch."

Life on the clearing seemed empty after that, without the dog. Sometimes, I'd stop and think about Rex, but not for long. I couldn't bear it. I couldn't understand this wanton cruelty in a grown man.

June passed. July set in hot and dry. Stuart held a Fourth of July picnic. The Reeders asked us to go with them, but it fell on a Wednesday and Papa said no.

We chopped cotton, hoed the corn and cane, and picked up dead limbs, and sawed them for firewood. The corn looked good, two ears on each stalk. We dug the potatoes. Papa learned that Sam Cashburn, who ran a grocery store at Gerty, had a brother in the Tulsa produce business. Papa contacted the man. He came down and bought one thousand pounds of potatoes. He handed Papa a crisp ten dollar bill. That was the biggest bill we'd seen in a long time.

My eyes widened. "Wow! Ten dollars! That would buy half of Stuart!"

"Yeah," Frank said, "if we could plant all this new ground into Irish potatoes next year, it'd make us rich."

I thought things were finally beginning to look up on the clearing, but a few days later, tragedy struck again.

Joe had gone out early to bring in Mike. At night, we tethered the mule outside the clearing, where he could graze on the grass. Joe came running back.

"Papa! Mike's in the cane field!"

We ran back with Joe. Someone had left the gate into the clearing down, or Mike knocked it down. We found the mule in the cane field, his stomach bloated from the green cane. He stumbled around and fell.

Papa rushed to him. "Somebody git me a bamboo stick!"

I ran back to the cabin and got one of the cane poles J.W. and I had cut to fish for perch, down on Boggy. Papa sharpened one end of the hollow tube with his pocket knife.

Papa knelt by Mike. "You boys hold him down."

I clutched Mike's head. Frank and Joe sat on his legs. Papa raised his knife and plunged the blade into Mike's distended stomach. The mule squealed in pain and tried to get up. Papa jabbed the stick into the opening he had cut. Foul gas hissed out. Mike laid back. He sank into a lethargy. Papa could not save him. Mike died.

We stood around and gazed in silence at the mule, the full impact of his death hitting us hard.

Papa's lips trembled. "I don't know how we're goin' to git another mule. We still owe ten dollars on this un." He sighed heavily. "Seems like it's gist somethin' all the time to take the joy out of living'." His gaze roamed the clearing. "Well, at least we got the crops laid by. That's somethin' to be thankful for. We won't need a mule now 'til fall. Maybe by then I can figger somethin'."

That afternoon, Joe and I walked over to Reeders' and borrowed Kate and Babe. We dragged Mike off into the woods. Papa piled brush on the mule and burned him.

It seemed to me like everything on the clearing was falling apart. One by one, our animals were dying. We didn't have the money to replace them, and the Depression showed few signs of relenting. Perry was gone. Opal acted stranger all the time. What could happen next?

For a time, things settled into a deceptive lull. Summer school started. Frank worked around a little, chopping cotton. He had grown more moody. He wasn't getting anywhere. I knew he wanted to marry Leota Ritter. How could he, though, when he felt Papa needed him? Perry would have walked off and done it anyway. Frank wasn't Perry.

One day, Leota and her sister Leta, who had married a prosperous McAlester real estate man, drove to the clearing in Leta's new Packard. Leta let Frank drive the Packard. His face beamed like that of a king, as he sat behind the steering wheel. Later, this little taste of luxury only added to his restlessness.

On top of that, Leota told him they were going to move up by Stony Point, fifteen miles from Stuart. How would he ever be able to see her up there?

Papa worried about getting another mule. Opal wouldn't mind anyone anymore and fought with the younger kids all the time. Mama looked drained, the heat and busy canning season sapping her strength. Everyone's nerves seemed on edge.

One hot Saturday afternoon, we all sat under the arbor, hoping a cool breeze might blow up. Betty, Hazel, and Opal drew pictures.

Betty held up her paper. "Look at my picture. Purty, ain't it?"

Opal snatched the paper. "Let me see. Oh, that ain't no good." She ripped the paper, wadded it up, and threw it away.

Papa's brow furrowed. "Opal, that ain't no way to behave. What's the matter with you? You're gittin' so you don't care about nothin' or nobody. I think it's 'bout time I straighten you out, young lady." He cut a hickory switch.

Opal faced him in open defiance. "Go ahead! I don't care. Whip me to death if you want to!"

Mama pressed her knuckles to her lips in fear.

Frank rose. "Papa, that won't do any good. Somethin's wrong with her."

"They'll be somethin' wrong with her, when I git through. Why don't you gist leave the runnin' of this family to me, young man? Wait 'til you git a family of your own before you go tellin' a-body how to raise his kids."

Papa may not have always been right, but he was always boss. He was letting Frank know it now in no uncertain terms.

His words cut Frank to the quick. They were the final straw. "A'right, if that's the way you feel 'bout it, I'll gist leave."

"That's fine with me," Papa said.

I knew Papa wasn't trying to get rid of Frank. It was the weather and everything in general. In Papa's own gruff way, he was telling Frank, "Okay, I've imposed on you long enough. I won't hold you any longer."

That was not the way Frank took it. "Yeah, now that the crops are laid by and the work's done, you're through with me."

Papa's mouth tightened. "You worked and bought that cow. She's yours and I told you, you could have her. But right now, we need her. So, there's ten dollars in there from the potatoes. It's all in the God's world we got, but you take it and go on."

"No, you keep it," Frank said. "I won't need it."

He went into the cabin and packed a small cardboard suitcase. I couldn't figure out how things had happened so fast. I didn't want Frank to go, yet I understood his longing to get out in the world and be on his own.

Mama sat with tears shimmering in her eyes. "Henry, you were too rough on him."

Papa sat down. He searched for words to express his

feelings. "I didn't mean to be rough on him. I'm not through with him as a son. I simply meant we had depended on him long enough. Too long. He's already done all he can to help us. If he wants to go, let him go."

"That is not what you told him," Mama said.

"Well, that's what I meant anyway," Papa said. "It don't mean I don't love him as a son. I'm gist turnin' him loose. He'll understand."

Frank didn't understand though Mama tried to explain. Papa's pride was too much to permit him to go to Frank himself. The break was complete. Frank got up early the next morning, slipped on his seersucker pants and yellow polo shirt. He left the cabin, carrying his suitcase. I followed him to the clearing gate.

"Rusty Guts, where you goin'?" I asked.

"Up to Tulsa, try to git on," he said.

"You ever comin' back?"

"I don't know." Frank's voice sounded empty and sadness filled his dark eyes. He paused and gazed around at the clearing. "I hate to leave home. I hate to leave Leota, all them good play parties, singings, dinner on the ground. I know times are hard. It's goin' to be hard to find a job, but I guess Papa and Mama and the rest of you are more secure now. Time for me to be movin' on. Bye, Tag." He paused for a long moment, the rising sun glinting on his wavy, black hair. "Don't let the Yahoos and painters getcha."

I nodded, my eyes misting. "Take care."

I watched Frank go up the road as Perry had done. Frank paused for a moment beside the lonesome pine. His melancholy song reached me on the still air:

"Oh, they cut down the old pine tree,
And hauled it away to the mill,
To make a coffin of pine . . . "

Then he was gone. I felt something had departed out of

the morning. The hillback to Boggy would never be the same.

July passed in a swelter of heat. The August sun blazed down. The corn and cane wilted in the hot, dry wind. Summer school drew to a close. The work on the clearing continued.

One day, Joe and I were sawing wood, clearing up some more new ground. Lem Hatcher cut across the lower end of the field, checking some of his cattle. We watched him in suspicion. He ambled over to us.

His shifty eyes darted away. "Heered your mule died."

"Yeah," Joe admitted cautiously.

"If I had that old mule, I'd make him so fat you couldn't see his ass."

I didn't like Hatcher, nor could I forgive him for what happened to Rex, but the way he said this, tickled me, and I had to laugh.

Hatcher eyed the clearing, taking note of all the new ground we had cleared the past two summers. "What your dad needs is a good, big farm. He's got all you boys. He needs to rent him a bottom farm som'ers. He could make a real farmer."

Joe nodded. "Maybe, when we git settled, in a year or two, we'll rent us a farm."

Hatcher gazed at us a moment, his thoughts unreadable. He turned on his heel and left.

I glanced at Joe. "What d'you reckon that was all about?"

Joe shook his head. "Don't know, but he's up to somethin'. I bet we find out soon enough."

We did. In a day or two, a black Packard rolled into the clearing. A tall, hawk-faced man, dressed in a dark suit, cowboy hat and boots, and a string tie, got out. Papa stepped out of the cabin to greet him. The rest of us clustered around the doorway.

"Mr. Speer? I'm D.M. Swink,* attorney over at McAlester." The visitor handed Papa a little, white card. "I represent the Black Diamond Mining Company who owns this land. You people are going to have to move."

The suddenness of the edict stunned us. Papa stared at the lawyer, then at the little, white card in his hand. "I – I can't move. There ain't no way I can move now."

The lawyer's lips twitched. "Mr. Speer, the company don't want people in here. You go building cabins, cribs, putting fences in here – well, that is improving the land. That raises the company's taxes. You'll have to move."

Papa struggled to gather his thoughts. "Well, I might move this winter if I can find a place, but I'm not goin' to move until I can gather my crops. I don't believe you can put me off here in less than ninety days."

The lawyer nodded, conceding the point. "Well, I'll tell you what you do, then. You go ahead and stay here, but the company doesn't want you here. You stay on until fall. You get what you've got gathered. Then you go somewhere and see if you can rent a place. I'll give you until November to vacate the premises."

Papa's shoulders slumped, his world crashing around him. "A'right, I'll do that."

The lawyer turned towards his car, then swung back. "Another thing, we don't want anybody in here making whiskey. I've heard there are people around here that make whiskey. You don't happen to know anything about that, do you?"

"No, I don't know anything. Nothin' but a lot of hearsay."

"Just what have you heard? This is just between you and me." The lawyer eyed Papa intently.

Papa hesitated. "Well, it's been rumored that Lem Hatcher down on Boggy makes whiskey and sells it, but I don't know. It's strictly hearsay far as I'm concerned."

The lawyer seemed satisfied. "Yes, I've heard that

---

*Name changed.

from other people. Those are the very birds we do not want in here." He smiled pleasantly and got in his car.

The Packard purred from the clearing. None of us said anything for a bit.

Mama twisted her hands. "Henry, what are we goin' to do?"

Papa shook his head. Weariness etched the deep lines in his face even deeper. "'*Man shall earn his bread by the sweat of his brow, all the days of his life.*'"

Joe glanced across the clearing. "I wonder how he found out we were here?"

None of us could venture a guess. Things looked bleak right then. The Depression was still on and now we were right back where we started, with no place to go and nothing on which to do it.

For a time, Papa did nothing. Mr. Swink started sending him notices, reminding him he had to move off. Papa walked all over the country looking for a place he could rent on shares. He could find none.

One Saturday, Papa happened to be in Harper's store in Stuart asking someone about a place. Mr. Harper overheard and told Papa he had a place about nine miles south of Stuart. It was the old Ed Davis place, where Jim Crosswaite lived. Mr. Harper wanted one hundred dollars a year, cash rent.

Papa didn't have that kind of money. Nevertheless, he said he would go by and look at it. He rode home with Albert and Loren Reeder in their wagon. They took him by the Harper place, a mile east of their own. Papa walked all around the farm. It had two big fields, a good four-room, clapboard house on it, two big springs, and plenty of wood. The fences were down and the barn needed mending, but those things were minor in his eyes.

That night, at the supper table, Papa asked if Joe and the rest of us thought we could work it without Frank.

"Don't guess we got any choice," Joe said. "We got to do somethin'."

The hassle started again. Where were we going to get a team, with which to work the farm? Where were we going to get the cash rent?

Next day, Papa went to Holdenville to see if he could borrow the money. The banker thought one hundred dollars a year was too much rent and would only loan him forty dollars against the next crop at twenty percent interest. Papa took it. On the way home, he called Bud in Tulsa. Bud told him to go ahead and rent the place. He would talk to the others up there and get the rest of the money to him by the end of the week.

So, Papa rented the place. The thought of living in a real house again excited us. Mama would not have far to go to wash. The boys could have their own room and the girls could, too. Each of us planned how we would fix them up.

"We're goin' to have curtains in our room," Betty bragged.

I smirked. "We don't want any of that old stuff. We're goin' to hang cowboy pictures on our wall."

"Now that we got a barn, maybe we can have a horse," Joe said.

"Yeah," I agreed, "we can cut wood on Saturday and buy a saddle!"

Things suddenly seemed not so grim.

Soon after we moved, that fall, Lem Hatcher took over the clearing. Later, Papa learned Hatcher had been behind the whole thing in getting us kicked off the place. Why, we were never sure. Perhaps Papa had scared him, when he had gone down there with the shotgun. More likely, Hatcher was afraid Papa would find his still and turn him over to the Federal authorities for illegal whiskey selling.

Whatever, Hatcher had made a special trip to McAlester. He asked around until he learned the name of the lawyer representing the Black Diamond Mine company. Hatcher struck up a bargain with Swink to supply him with all the whiskey he wanted in "dry" Oklahoma. In return, Swink promised to rent him the clearing for twenty-eight dollars a year. Hatcher had been the "very bird" Swink *had* wanted in there. The following spring, Hatcher planted corn in the bountiful new ground. He burned down the two cribs and the cabin that Papa, Joe, and Perry had worked so hard to build.

Sometimes, when I thought about all the work we had put into the clearing for nothing, it made me angry. Papa had taught us to live by the golden rule. When we did, others had taken advantage of us.

However, in time, I came to look back on those hard months our family spent on a hillback to Boggy as the greatest adventure of my life.

Then that summer of 1934, after we moved, the Great Depression deepened. The whole country seemed in desperate straits. Again, I wondered what would happen to us. One thing I knew for certain. The past two years had tried and tested us. In the future, as long as the family stayed together, Papa held the reins, and kept his faith in the Lord, we would survive.

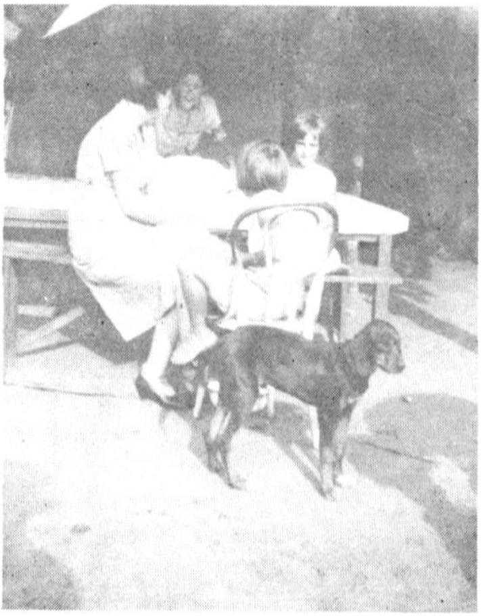

Sitting before the tent, beneath the brush arbor, Laura Speer takes time to visit with her daughter-in-law, Drucy Speer, while daughters, Betty (on chair), and Hazel listen. The dog is Rex.

Photo courtesy of Jess Speer.

Henry Speer plays with the dogs that were so important to the family's livelihood. Deadened trees stand in the new ground, and at the far side of the clearing are the cribs which became rat infested.

Photo courtesy of Jess Speer

Dressed in his coveralls, Pete Speer stands on the running-board of the new Whippet automobile, which the family was forced to abandon in Tulsa, during the Great Depression.

Photo courtesy of Jess Speer.

Frank Speer, about 1940. Frank felt a dedication to the family and stayed on the clearing to help them though he longed to move out on his own and get married.

Photo courtesy of Jess Speer

Perry was argumentative and always trying to get Papa to move to California. During the Depression, he hoboed a lot.

Photo courtesy of Jess Speer.

Joe was quiet and dependable. He took over when Papa was not home.

Opal Speer, l., could never accept the destitute condition in which the family found itself. Others shown are Archie Bolaski, a neighbor in Tulsa, and a niece, Wanda McClure.

The Reeder family, who helped the Speer family on the Hillback To Boggy and remained their life-long friends. Back row, left to right: C.C. Reeder, a former Texas Ranger, Mrs. Reeder, Albert, Pansy, Loren. Front row: J.W., and Zenora.

Photo courtesy of Jess Speer.

The class of 1935 at Bohannon School, Hughes County, Oklahoma. The teachers are, l., Cleburn Pounds, grades one to four, and Charley Watson, grades five to eight. From left to right the students are:

Top Row: George Lanham, Eloise Huddleston, Naomi Christian, Floyce McNutt, Juanita Elwood, Willa Crosswait, Geneva Lane. Second Row: Bertha Lanham, Mary Cullem, Paul Reeder, Tag Speer, J.W. Reeder, J.B. Crosswait, Charley Mills, Harley Lane. Third Row: Zenora Reeder, Betty Speer, Pauline Jones, Clifford Lane, __, Harold McNutt, Kenneth Tramel. Fourth Row: Orpha May Reeder, Joyce Crosswait, __, Hazel Speer, Rayford Overton, __, __, Taylor Lanham, L. D. Hull. Fifth Row: Bertha Lanham, __, Gene Jones, Dot Gould, Calvin Reeder, J.W. Lane, Everett Christian, Scott Mills, Bob Jones, Kenneth Huddleston. Front Row, (sitting) fourth from left, Pete Speer.

Photo courtesy of Jess Speer.